CONTENTS

GRADE 5

i

McGraw-Hill School Division

The Marble Champ

The Paper Dragon

Grandma Essie's Covered Wagon

Going Back Home

A Mountain of a Monument

McGraw-Hill School Division

Carlos and the Skunk

How to Think Like A Scientist

Island Scrapbook

The Big Storm

Catching Up with Lewis and Clark

McGraw-Hill School Division

Unit 5: BRIGHT IDEAS

The Riddle

Life in Flatland

Tonweya and the Eagles

Breaker's Bridge

Cleaning Up America's Air

McGraw-Hill School Division

Amistad Rising

Rip Van Winkle

Sea Maidens of Japan

The Silent Lobby

Amazon Alert!

McGraw-Hill School Division

Problem and Solution

The **plot** is made up of the main events that happen in the story. In most stories the main character faces a **problem** and must find a **solution** for it. Read the story, and answer each question.

"Jonas," Sara said excitedly to her brother. "Let's go to the aquarium. We can see the sharks and the new baby whale! But I don't have any money."

"I have enough money to buy tickets for the aquarium or take the bus, but not for both," said Jonas.

"We can get free passes from the library for the aquarium. Then we can use your money for the bus," said Sara. "How's that?"

"Fine, but you still have to pay me back," said Jonas. "Or you could clean my room? How's that for a deal?"

"Sounds good to me," Sara said and nodded. Then they ran to the library to get their passes.

1. Where did Sara want to go? _____

2. What was her problem? _____

3. Why did she think Jonas could solve her problem? _____

_____

4. What was Jonas' problem? _____

5. What was the solution? What extra benefit did Jonas get? _____

_____

_____

5 | Book 5/Unit 1
The Wise Old Woman

At Home: Have students tell about a time they had to work for something.

1

Vocabulary

Select the correct word from the choices in parentheses. Then write the correct word on the line provided.

1. The crops were plentiful, and the farmers (prospered, perished). _____

2. The mayor (summoned, dismissed) the winners to receive their award. _____

3. We hung our school (books, banner) in the auditorium to celebrate winning the

   game. _____

4. She had finally (conquered, quit) her fear of horses and rode one in the parade.

   _____

5. The ancient (statue, scroll) contained the story of a famous king. _____

At Home: Have students use each vocabulary word in a
story that takes place long ago.

Book 5/Unit 1
The Wise Old Woman ⬜ 5

The Tale of the Weaver

Long ago, a weaver was looking for work. He saw an old and torn *banner* flying from a castle. The weaver knew he could weave a beautiful one. He went to the castle. A large guard was standing outside.

The weaver *summoned* his courage and asked to see the king. The king *reluctantly* agreed to see him. On the walls were banners showing the lands the king had *conquered.*

The king handed the weaver a *scroll* and told him to weave a banner depicting the story written on it. The weaver used his most beautiful yarns to create the banner. The king loved it and rewarded the weaver. The weaver *prospered* and lived happily ever after.

1. What did the weaver see outside the castle? _____

2. Why did the weaver decide to see the king? _____

_____

3. What vocabulary word describes how the king felt about seeing the weaver?

_____

4. What does the king hand to the weaver? What does the king want the weaver to

weave? _____

_____

5. Why do you think the weaver *prospered*? _____

_____

_____

McGraw-Hill School Division

5 Book 5/Unit 1
The Wise Old Woman   **At Home:** Have students create a banner
for their room.   **2a**

Story Comprehension

Answer the following questions about "The Wise Old Woman."

1. Why does the young farmer have to take his mother into the mountains?

_____

_____

2. How does the young farmer save his mother? _____

_____

_____

3. What happens to the cruel village lord? _____

_____

_____

4. How does the wise old woman save herself and her village? _____

_____

_____

5. What does the cruel lord learn ? _____

_____

_____

At Home: Have students write about an older
person they know and tell why they respect him or her.

McGraw-Hill School Division

Use Parts of a Book

Books can have many different parts. Write the name of a **part of a book** in order to answer each question.

Front of the book	Back of the book
title page	glossary
table of contents	index
copyright page	

1. What can you find on the title page of a book? _____

   _____

   _____

2. Which book part is like a small dictionary? _____

3. How can you find the first page number of a chapter? _____

   _____

4. Which part tells when a book was published? _____

   _____

5. Which two parts are arranged in alphabetical order? _____

   _____

6. How do you know if a topic or information you need is not in a book? _____

   _____

   _____

6 Book 5/Unit 1
The Wise Old Woman

At Home: Have students locate a book and point out its parts to a family member.

4

Problem and Solution

The **plot** is what happens in a story. In some stories, an important part of plot is how characters find **solutions** to **problems** they face. Write **T** if the statement correctly describes how a problem is solved in "The Wise Old Woman." Write **F** if the statement does not correctly describe how a problem is solved in "The Wise Old Woman."

_____ 1. The young farmer hides his mother.

_____ 2. The six wisest people of the village complete the tasks.

_____ 3. The mother completes the tasks.

_____ 4. The young farmer shows the lord completed tasks.

_____ 5. When Lord Higa sees that the tasks have been completed, he still decides

to conquer the village.

In folktales like "The Wise Old Woman" there are often three main events or **problems**. Write the **solutions** to the three main problems in the story.

1. The young farmer does not want his mother to die. _____

_____

2. The young farmer wants to hide his mother. _____

_____

_____

3. The three impossible tasks must be done to save the village. _____

_____

_____

At Home: Have students write a difficult task for their family members or friends to solve.

McGraw-Hill School Division

Make Inferences

An **inference** is a conclusion or deduction made from evidence. You make inferences about story elements based on details in the story or your own experience. Answer the questions by making inferences about the story below.

Peter loved horses. His dream was to catch a wild horse and train it. One day his uncle invited him to go with him to find wild horses. Peter was thrilled. He would find his dream horse.

Peter worked hard to keep up with his uncle and the crew of cowhands. He didn't complain. They spotted a herd of wild horses. Peter saw the horse he wanted. It was a beautiful, black stallion.

Peter watched how the cowhands captured the horses. They were good at their jobs. But he saw how sad the horses looked once they were caught. Peter put his rope away. There would be no wild horse for him.

1. In what part of the country does this story probably take place? _____

_____

2. How would you describe Peter? _____

_____

3. Why could Peter be called caring? _____

_____

4. How do the cowhands feel about capturing the horses? _____

_____

_____

5. What do you think Peter will say to his uncle about his horse? _____

_____

_____

At Home: Have students write about a dream they have had and how it has changed as they have grown older.

Synonyms and Antonyms

Synonyms are words with the same or similar meanings. **Antonyms** are words with opposite or nearly opposite meanings.

Write a synonym to replace each underlined word.

wise	woman	beautiful	completed

1. The <u>smart</u>, old woman told wonderful stories. _____

2. The <u>lady</u> played us a song on her electric guitar. _____

3. The flowers looked very <u>pretty</u> in that vase. _____

4. At first she felt as though she would never get <u>done</u> with the long hike, but she

   was proud of herself when she finally _____ it.

Write an antonym to replace each underlined word.

young	smart	kind	question

5. He was <u>old</u>, but he acted _____.

6. Sometimes he acts <u>stupid</u>, although we all know he is really very _____.

7. One brother was extremely <u>cruel</u>, while the other one was _____.

8. He gave the wrong <u>answer</u>, because he hadn't heard the _____.

At Home: Have students write sentences using these
synonyms and antonyms.

McGraw-Hill School Division

Story Elements

The **setting** is when and where the story occurs. The **characters** are who the story is about. The **plot** is what happens in the story.

Read the story. Then answer the questions in the chart.

Soon-Yi and her brother Kyung-Bu hurried along the empty, city street. They were rushing to the bakery. Every Saturday morning their family would have fresh, warm muffins for breakfast. Soon-Yi and Kyung-Bu were hungry. Their family was waiting impatiently at home.

It was a warm, spring day. As they walked along, Kyung-Bu spotted a skinny kitten lying by the side of a brick building. "Look at that kitten!" said Kyung-Bu. "I think it needs help."

Soon-Yi took off her jacket and wrapped it around the kitten. "Let's take it to the veterinarian down the block," she said. They hurried off to the vet's office.

"I'll treat your kitten," said the vet. "But I can't do it for free." Soon-Yi and Kyung-Bu looked at each other and smiled. They paid with the muffin money. There would be no warm muffins. Instead they had a new family member.

Setting	Characters
1. Where does the story first take place? _____ _____	4. Who are the main characters.? _____ _____
2. When does the story take place? _____	5. How would you describe the personalities of Soon-Yi and Kyung-Bu? _____
3. What important decisions do Soon-Yi and Kyung-Bu make? Explain. _____ _____	6. From what you know of Soon-Yi and Kyung-Bu, do you think the family will keep the kitten? Explain. _____ _____ _____

6 Book 5/Unit 1
The Voyage of the *Dawn Treader*

At Home: Have students identify the setting and the characters in one of their favorite books.

8

Vocabulary

Label each sentence **True** or **False.** If a sentence is false, explain why on the line below.

1. A *bruised* ankle turns a dark color. _____
   _____

2. Having to wait seven hours for the train was a real *convenience*. _____
   _____

3. Polite people try not to *offend* others. _____
   _____

4. A letter of protest shows that you *approve* of something. _____
   _____

5. If you are invited somewhere, that means your *presence* is wanted. _____
   _____

6. A good friend's face is only *vaguely* familiar. _____
   _____

At Home: Have students write a sentence using each of the vocabulary words.

Book 5/Unit 1
Voyage of the *Dawn Treader* / 6

McGraw-Hill School Division

Doctor's Orders

The school nurse looked up from her charts at Bill. He looked *vaguely* familiar, but she wasn't quite sure how she knew him. She smiled at him. He was the same age as her son. She saw right away that the area around his left eye was *bruised*.

"Not that I mean to *offend* you," she said, "but what on earth did you do to that eye?"

"I fell off my skateboard," explained Bill. "I took a turn too fast and fell onto a rock." To himself, Bill wondered if the nurse might not *approve* of skateboarding. Some people thought it was a dangerous sport, though Bill always wore his helmet and was usually careful.

The nurse examined Bill's eye. "We have at our *convenience* the services of an excellent eye doctor in town. I want you to see her right now."

"But I have soccer practice in 15 minutes!" protested Bill.

"Your *presence* on the field can wait. It's more important to get your eye checked as soon as possible," she replied firmly.

1. What does a *bruised* eye look like? _____

_____

2. What is a word that means "not clearly or distinctly"? _____

3. What does it mean to *offend* someone? _____

_____

4. What does the word *convenience* mean in this story? _____

_____

5. Why doesn't the nurse approve of Bill's going to soccer now? _____

_____

_____

5 Book 5/Unit 1
Voyage of the *Dawn Treader*

At Home: Have students write about something that is a convenience for them.

9a

McGraw-Hill School Division

Story Comprehension

A story map can help you analyze the elements of a story. Story elements include characters, setting, and plot. The **characters** are the people in the story. They help create the **plot**, or the series of events that happen. The **setting** is the particular time and place in which the story occurs. Think about the story elements in "The Voyage of the *Dawn Treader*." Then complete the story map below. For help you may look back at the story.

Title: The Voyage of the *Dawn Treader*

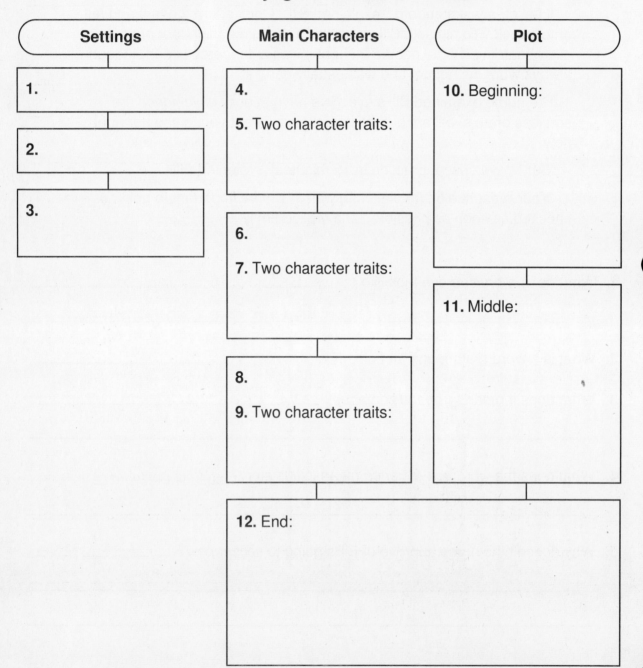

Settings	Main Characters	Plot
1.	4. 5. Two character traits:	10. Beginning:
2.	6. 7. Two character traits:	11. Middle:
3.	8. 9. Two character traits:	
	12. End:	

At Home: Have students discuss whether or not they think Reepicheep responded appropriately to Eustace's insulting behavior.

10

Book 5/Unit 1
Voyage of the *Dawn Treader*

12

McGraw-Hill School Division

Use a Glossary

A **glossary** is the part of a book that defines important words found in the book. Answer the questions below about using a glossary.

1. Where do you find a glossary? _____

2. How is a glossary the same as a small dictionary? _____

_____

3. How is a glossary different from a small dictionary? _____

_____

4. How are words listed in a glossary? _____

5. Where are guide words located? _____

_____

6. How are guide words useful? _____

_____

7. Which of your school books has a glossary? Why? _____

_____

_____

8. If a glossary tells you what a word means, why might you look the word up in a

dictionary, too? _____

_____

_____

Story Elements

Answer the questions about **setting** and **characters** in the chart below.

Setting	Characters
1. Where are Lucy and Edmund spending the summer? _____ _____ _____ _____	4. How does Eustace act when he meets Reepicheep? _____ _____ _____ _____
2. How do you think the story would be if there was no painting on the wall? _____ _____ _____	5. What kind of friends do you think Lucy and Edmund would be? _____ _____ _____ _____
3. What does the cabin that Lucy changed her clothes in look like? _____ _____	6. What made Caspian think that he should get his guests dry clothes and warmed up? _____ _____

Cause and Effect

Events in a story are connected to each other. A **cause** is the reason why something happens, and an **effect** is the result, or what happens.

Read the paragraph below. Then draw a line between the cause and its matching effect.

Today was an important day. It was Marco's first day on a new job. He shouldn't have been late. But he was. Marco was in a hurry because his alarm clock didn't go off. But it wasn't his fault. The electricity had gone out overnight. Luckily his cat woke him up because she wanted to be fed. He had to rush.

Marco had planned on taking his time and walking to work, but since he was running late he couldn't. Marco sighed. He would have to use his lunch money for a taxi cab. He had had no time to make a lunch, so he would have to go without it today. Marco raced out the door when the cab honked. When he got in, he thought his shirt felt funny, but he didn't check it. Instead he sat and worried.

Finally Marco got to work. He raced in the door. The receptionist smiled at him. Then she said, "You might want to fix your shirt. It's on backwards."

Cause	**Effect**
1. The electricity goes out overnight.	a. Marco finally wakes up.
2. The alarm doesn't go off.	b. Marco's shirt is on backwards.
3. His cat wants to be fed.	c. He has to take a cab to work.
4. He doesn't have enough time to walk to work.	d. The alarm doesn't go off.
5. Marco is in a rush and doesn't check his appearance.	e. Marco wakes up late and has to hurry.

5

Book 5/Unit 1
Wilma Unlimited

At Home: Have students identify cause-and-effect in their favorite book of fiction.

15

Vocabulary

Supply the correct word from the list.

| astounding | athletic | bushel | concentrating | luxury | scholarship |

1. Jen was a very talented painter, but she couldn't afford to pay for college. Luckily,

   Jen won a big _____ to one of the best art colleges. .

2. Sometimes it is fun to treat yourself to a _____ item, such as an

   expensive meal or a vacation.

3. The crowd gave the band a thunderous cheer. They thought the band was

   _____ .

4. The large basket held a _____ of peaches.

5. The school work was so hard that it required all his attention. Bill's furrowed brow

   was a sign of how much he was _____ .

6. The coach picked players for their _____ ability, and for their team spirit.

Grandmother Kate

When my grandmother Kate was little, she worked on her grandfather's farm picking fruits at harvest time with her friends. It was hard work. They had to pick a lot of fruit to fill a *bushel* basket.

Picking fruit was fun, too. My grandmother and her friends used to make up *athletic* contests to pass the time. She said some of the tricks of her friends were *astounding*. One friend climbed a tree very fast, and another pitched the rotten fruit into a barrel with extreme accuracy.

When my grandmother was not picking fruit, she was *concentrating* on her drawing. She used to use charcoals and watercolors, because oil paints were considered a *luxury*. She spent many hours practicing her painting. In fact, she became such a good painter she won an art *scholarship*!

1. What kind of basket might you use to hold a lot of fruit? _____

2. What made the work *athletic?*_____

3. How did painting help grandmother win a *scholarship*? _____

_____

4. What word could be replaced with the word "focusing"? _____

5. Why might oil paints be a *luxury*? _____

_____

McGraw-Hill School Division

5

Book 5/Unit 1
Wilma Unlimited

At Home: Have students write about what they do to help at home or describe a hobby.

16a

Story Comprehension

Read each sentence. Write **T** if the statement is true and based on facts from "Wilma Unlimited." Write **F** if the statement is false or incorrect.

_____ **1.** Wilma was the oldest of 19 children.

_____ **2.** Wilma was so underweight when she was born that people thought she would not live to see her first birthday.

_____ **3.** Wilma was so sickly as a child that she never ran or jumped around the way most children do.

_____ **4.** Wilma was almost five years old when she became sick with polio.

_____ **5.** Everyone was confident that Wilma would recover from polio and walk and play again.

_____ **6.** Wilma had to do exercises to make her leg strong enough to use again.

_____ **7.** The school welcomed Wilma even though she was paralyzed and couldn't walk or use her leg.

_____ **8.** Wilma continued doing leg exercises, even though it hurt, because she was determined to get stronger, and this helped her.

_____ **9.** The first time Wilma walked without her brace was when she stepped onto the basketball court.

_____ **10.** Wilma was twelve years old before she could walk without the aid of a leg brace.

At Home: Have students write about an experience either playing or watching sports.

Use an Index

Most nonfiction books have an **index**—an alphabetical list of topics—located at the back of a book. Index entries often have subtopics indented underneath. A sample index is shown below. Use the index to answer each question.

B
baleen whales
   See whales, toothless
blubber, 256
blue whales, 257
 	
C
cetaceans, 252, 264, 265
 	
D
dolphins, 253, 264
dugongs, 256
 	
E
echolocation, 261-262
 	
F
flukes, 254
	G
	gray whales, 257, 270-271
	
	M
	manatees, 256
	marine mammals
	   behavior, 264
	   communication, 264-265
	   migration, 270
	   reproduction, 271-273
	   swimming and diving, 259, 275
	
	P
	pods, 257
	polar bears, 253
	porpoises, 253
		S
		sea lions, 251
		sea otters, 253
		seals, 251
		
		W
		walruses, 251
		whales
		   fossils of, 252, 254
		   gray whales, 257, 270-271
		   migration of, 260
		   right whales, 257
		   toothed, 256, 258
		   toothless, 256
		   types of, 256-259

1. On which page(s) are sea otters discussed? _____

2. Which two entries in the index have subentries? _____

3. On which page(s) will you find information about whale fossils? _____

4. Which page(s) should you read to find out what echolocation is? _____

5. Under which entry should you look to find information about baleen whales? _____

_____

6. Does this book contain an entry for mythical sea creatures? Explain. _____

_____

7. On which page(s) would you find out how marine mammals swim? _____

8. Under which two entries could you look for information about gray whales? _____

_____

At Home: Have students find a book with an index and demonstrate how to use it.

Cause and Effect

A **cause** is the reason why something happens. An **effect** is the result, or what happens. Many story events are connected through cause-and-effect relationships. In each sentence, the cause is underlined.

Add the effect for each of the story events below.

1. **Cause:** Every weekend, in all types of weather, Ellen prepared for the basketball team tryouts. <u>She spent hours practicing.</u> She practiced even when her friends went to the movies or did other things.

   Effect: _____

2. **Cause:** Robby and Neeta were supposed to have cleaned the kitchen before their mother got home from work. Only then could they go out skateboarding. When their mother came home, however, <u>the kitchen was still a mess.</u>

   Effect: _____

   _____

3. **Cause:** Saturday morning Amber borrowed a bicycle from her cousin Shannon. She promised to return it by Sunday morning so Shannon could use it in the bike race. <u>Amber returned the bike early Saturday night.</u>

   Effect: _____

4. **Cause:** It was a good night for camping, since the weather was clear and not too cold. The stars were shining brightly. There was just one problem. <u>They forgot the tent.</u>

   Effect: _____

5. **Cause:** Ekwe was feeling a little sad. He had just missed the bus and wouldn't be able to meet his friends in time for the movie they planned to see. Suddenly <u>his friend's mother drove up in her van</u>. "Need a lift?" she asked.

   Effect: _____

   _____

At Home: Have students write a story with a clear cause-and-effect relationship.   Book 5/Unit 1
Wilma Unlimited /5

Problem and Solution

Characters find **solutions** to the **problems** they face in a story. Read the story below. Then complete the story chart.

Zack is late for school. He decides to use his skateboard in order to get to school quickly. Besides, he needs it for his skateboarding contest later in the afternoon. Zack skates right past the principal. She calls Zack over. There is no skateboarding allowed in the schoolyard. She takes his skateboard.

During study hall, Zack asks to see the principal. He promises to work for the next week planting flower beds, if he can get back his skateboard. Since Zack has never been in trouble before, she finally agrees. Zack takes his skateboard and goes to the competition.

Before the race starts, Zack discovers the back wheel is stiff. He needs to loosen the bolt and oil the wheel. He grabs the skateboard and runs back to the school. He finds the custodian who helps him fix his wheel. Zack races back just in time for the competition.

Problem	Solution
1. Zack is late for school.	
2. The principal takes Zack's skateboard.	
3. Zack's wheel is stiff.	
4. Zack needs to find someone to help him fix the back wheel.	

At Home: Have students write about a problem they have solved.

Context Clues

You can define an unknown word by using the words surrounding it to give you clues to the word's meaning.

Circle the **context clues** in each sentence that can help you figure out the meaning of the underlined word.

1. The name of the illness <u>pneumonia</u> comes from the ancient Greek word for lung.

2. Today children take a vaccine for <u>polio</u>, a disease that once paralyzed many children.

3. David pushed the heavy cart, in order to <u>propel</u> it forward.

4. After days alone, she felt <u>exhilarated</u> to be with her friends again. Their company made her feel happy and greatly cheered her.

5. The ski lift headed up the <u>slope</u>. After they got off the lift, the group prepared to ski down the mountainside.

6. The heat looked like a <u>shimmering</u> pool on the highway. You could almost see the light like it was glittering waves.

7. No one with any intelligence would turn down an award like that! It's not very often that people get a full college <u>scholarship</u>. That's a free education.

8. The couple won an expensive vacation in Europe. They considered the trip a <u>luxury</u> because they could have never afforded it if they had to pay for it!

McGraw-Hill School Division

Story Elements

The **setting** is when and where a story takes place. The **characters** are the people the story is about.

Read the story. Then complete the story chart.

Jamal walked alone by the river. Jamal missed his friends, and wished his family hadn't moved. It was late summer, and it was too late to sign up for anything. Jamal hadn't made any new friends because he was so shy. He soon saw some kids playing soccer in the park. They were good, but not great. Jamal wished they would ask him to play. But no one did.

The next day Jamal went to the park again. The same kids were playing soccer. Jamal watched them play. Suddenly the soccer ball rolled past him towards the river. Jamal heard the kids yelling. Quickly he stopped the ball and kicked it back. It was a perfect kick. The kids started playing again. As Jamal was leaving, one of the kids shouted at him, "Hey, that was a great kick. You play soccer?" Jamal nodded.

"Well, I'm Josephena, you want to play with us tomorrow?" the kid asked. Jamal smiled and said, "Sure."

Setting	Characters
1. Where does the story take place? _____ _____	4. How would you describe Jamal? _____ _____
2. When does the story take place? _____ _____	5. Did you think Jamal will make new friends? Why? _____ _____ _____
3. Do you think this story takes place today?. Explain. _____ _____ _____ _____	6. Do you think Jamal and Josephena will become friends? _____ _____ _____

6 Book 5/Unit 1
Wreck of the *Zephyr*

At Home: Have students write a story about Jamal and his new friend.

22

Vocabulary

Write a vocabulary word to replace the underlined word or words.

hull	ominous	shoreline	spire	timbers	treacherous

1. The <u>sides and bottom</u> of the boat needed to be repaired. _____

2. The view of the <u>coast</u> was an amazing sight from the helicopter. _____

3. The big storm stripped off the sides of the house, leaving only the <u>wood frame</u> standing. _____

4. The <u>threatening</u> clouds caused us to cancel the boat ride. _____

5. The church <u>steeple</u> rose above the town center. _____

6. The waves looked extremely <u>dangerous</u>. _____

At Home: Have students use the vocabulary words in new sentences.

McGraw-Hill School Division

The Storm

Luis loved being on a fishing ship. He slept in the *hull* of the boat with the other sailors. They treated him like a son and taught him how to fish. Luis loved looking at the *shoreline* from the boat deck. He could see the church's *spire* shining in the sunlight. At night, he stared at the stars.

One day the clouds began to look *ominous*. The sailors told him to stay below. Luis could feel the *timbers* of the boat shake. It was a *treacherous* storm. The boat rocked back and forth. Then suddenly it was calm. The sailors called Luis to come up to the main deck. There Luis saw a beautiful rainbow, and in the ocean he saw dolphins swimming. Luis smiled. This was why he loved being on the ocean.

1. What kind of storm was it? _____

2. What does Luis love looking at? _____

3. Why did the timbers of the boat shake? _____

   _____

4. Why do you think Luis sleeps in the hull? _____

   _____

5. Why might a storm at sea seem so ominous? Why does Luis still love the ocean?

   _____

   _____

   _____

   _____

5 Book 5/Unit 1
Wreck of the *Zephyr*

At Home: Have students write about a storm, real or pretend, they or someone they know has experienced.

23a

Story Comprehension

Complete each sentence by adding the number of the word or words that form a true statement about a character in "The Wreck of the *Zephyr*."

> **1.** The narrator
>
> **2.** The boy
>
> **3.** When the sailor on the island
>
> **4.** The old man

a _____ took the tiller, the boat began to lift out of the water.

b _____ told a story about the *Zephyr* and how it ended up on some cliffs high above the sea.

c _____ wanted to prove to the villagers—to the sea—what a great sailor he was.

d _____ took a walk after lunch and came across an unusual sight—the wreck of a small sailboat on the edge of some cliffs.

On the lines provided write a brief paragraph summarizing "The Wreck of the *Zephyr*."

_____

_____

_____

_____

_____

_____

_____

_____

_____

_____

At Home: Have students write a paragraph about what messages or themes "The Wreck of the *Zephyr*" might be exploring. Explain that a theme is a story's overall subject and meaning.

McGraw-Hill School Division

Use a Table of Contents and Headings

A **Table of Contents and Headings** tells you what a book is about and how the book's information is organized. Most nonfiction books have a table of contents and their chapters have headings. Read the sample and answer the questions.

TABLE OF CONTENTS

Chapter Number	Chapter Title	Page Number
1	Space Exploration	3
2	Prospects for Development	16
3	Planning Space Stations	38
4	The Final Frontier Expanding	65

Chapter 3: Planning Space Stations
Safe Habitats in Space

In planning a space station, it is important to build it so that people can survive there. Therefore, the space station must have a special design.

Growing Space Crops

Since there is a limited amount of room on the station, animals will not be raised as a food source. People living on the space station will grow crops, such as soy beans, to supply nutrition.

1. How many chapters are in the book? _____

2. What is the title of chapter 2? _____

3. On which page does chapter 4 begin? _____

4. What does the second heading in chapter 3 discuss? _____

5. Why is it a good idea to read the chapter headings before starting a new chapter?

_____

At Home: Have students locate the table of contents and chapter headings in nonfiction books, magazines, or texts.

Story Elements

The **setting** of a story is where and when events occur. The setting often has an effect on the **characters**. Consider how the settings affected the boy in "The Wreck of the *Zephyr*." Then answer the questions below.

Setting: Years ago, in a fishing village

1. The boy says that he is the greatest sailor there is and laughs as he hoists his sails into the blustery wind. Why does he feel he has to prove his sailing abilities in his village? _____

_____

2. What did the boy always want to prove to the villagers? _____

_____

Setting: The mysterious island

3. What was strange and magical about the island? _____

_____

4. Everyone in the village can fly their boats. Why does the boy insist he has to learn to do this before he leaves? _____

_____

5. The boy sails at night, trying to prove he is the best. But what does he prove?

_____

Setting: Back in the village, before and after the crash

6. What happens when the boy tries to fly over his village? _____

_____

7. How did the boy's visit to the mysterious island affect the rest of his life? _____

_____

8. How has the mysterious island changed the way people see the boy? _____

_____

At Home: Have students write about how the settings affect the boy.

McGraw-Hill School Division

Make Inferences

An **inference** is a conclusion or deduction made from evidence. You make inferences about story elements based on details in the story or your own experience. Read the story, and then answer the questions.

On the bus trip to the Museum of Natural History, best friends Tanika and Lew sat side by side. When the bus stopped so the class could eat lunch, Lew realized he'd forgotten his lunch. As usual, Tanika gave Lew half of her sandwich. Tanika often shared her lunch with Lew.

Lew and Tanika loved the museum. Lew bought a book on space in the gift shop. Tanika wanted to buy a piece of amber, but she didn't have enough money. As they left the museum, Lew noticed the look of disappointment on Tanika's face.

Back on the bus, Tanika noticed Lew was late. Suddenly, he jumped on the bus and thrust a package into Tanika's hands. She opened it. It was the amber! She noticed that Lew's book was gone.

"Oh, Thank you," Tanika said. Lew just smiled.

1. Lew forgets his lunch and, as usual, Tanika shares her lunch with him. What does that tell you about Lew's habits? _____

_____

2. Why does Tanika share her lunch with Lew? _____

_____

3. Why does Lew care about Tanika's feelings? _____

_____

4. How would you describe Lew at the end of the story? _____

_____

5. What inferences can you make about Tanika and Lew's friendship? _____

_____

5 Book 5/Unit 1
Wreck of the Zephyr

At Home: Have students make some inferences about Tanika and Lew and tell if they would want to be their friends.

27

Synonyms and Antonyms

Synonyms are words with the same or similar meanings. **Antonyms** are words with opposite or nearly opposite meanings. Use the following words to create two pairs of synonyms and antonyms.

even	familiar	odd	story	unknown	tale	wind	zephyr

Synonyms   **Antonyms**

_____   _____

_____   _____

Are the pair of underlined words in each sentence antonyms or synonyms? Write the answers on the lines.

1. A <u>zephy</u>r is a gentle <u>wind</u> that blows from the west. _____

2. I have heard that <u>story</u> so many times that I call it a "stale <u>tale</u>"! _____

3. The book sounded <u>familiar</u>, but the author was <u>unknown</u> to me. _____

4. He played on the <u>odd</u>-numbered team, and I played on the <u>even</u>-numbered team. _____

At Home: Have students use a thesaurus to find an antonym or synonym for each vocabulary word in "The Wreck of the Zephyr."

Book 5/Unit 1
Wreck of the *Zephyr*

12

Cause and Effect

A **cause** is the reason why something happens. An **effect** is the result, or what happens. Many story events are connected through cause-and-effect.

Read the story below. Then write the effect next to each cause.

Herman the clown used five trained monkeys in his circus act. At night he kept them in a monkey house, which he locked with a padlock. One day he noticed the lock was broken, so he decided to go to town to buy a new one. But Herman was afraid the monkeys might escape while he was gone, so he asked Dan, the sword eater, if he would watch his monkeys. As soon as Dan said yes, Herman drove into town.

While Herman was in town, Dan fell asleep. The monkeys escaped and walked down the road to town. When Herman returned from town, he was surprised to see his monkeys climbing in the trees next to the road. Herman stopped his car and called to them, but the monkeys were having too much fun to come down. Luckily, he had also bought some bananas for his monkeys. He offered them the bananas, and they scampered down from the trees and into his car. Herman quickly shut the doors and drove them home. With the monkeys safely in their house, Herman put on the new padlock.

Cause	Effect
1. Herman notices the broken lock.	**1.** _____ _____
2. Herman is afraid the monkeys might escape.	**2.** _____ _____
3. Dan falls asleep.	**3.** _____
4. The monkeys escape.	**4.** _____ _____
5. Herman offers the monkeys bananas.	**5.** _____ _____
6. He puts on the new padlock.	**6.** _____ _____

McGraw-Hill School Division

6 | Book 5/Unit 1
Tornadoes!

At Home: Have students write a short story in which one event triggers a whole series of events.

29

Vocabulary

Choose the correct word from the box to complete each sentence below.

destruction	detect	predictions	reliable	severe	stadium

1. It was a _____ wind storm that knocked down telephone and electrical wires.

2. Our team captain has to be a _____ person that we can all depend on.

3. So many people were expected at the summer jazz festival that they held it in a _____.

4. How does the smell of honey help you _____ where a bee's nest is?

5. Do your _____ really tell the future?

6. The hurricane caused so much _____ that it took years to rebuild the seaport town.

30
At Home: Have students write sentences using the vocabulary words.

Book 5/Unit 1
Tornadoes! / 6

McGraw-Hill School Division

The Football Game

We were watching a game at the football *stadium* when a *severe* storm struck. People had to run for cover because no one had an umbrella or raincoat. We were expecting a sunny day. The forecaster's *predictions* were all wrong! Usually his weather reports were *reliable*, but he didn't *detect* this storm on his radar screen. Luckily, the storm was short, causing little *destruction*. The game began again an hour later. The sun was shining and the storm was forgotten as we cheered for our team.

1. What are statements that tell you about future events called? _____
_____

2. What is a *severe* storm like? _____
_____

3. What sort of structure can hold many people and a football field? _____

4. How much *destruction* did the storm cause? _____

5. Why is it important to be able to detect storms and get reliable weather forecasts?

_____

_____

_____

5

Book 5/Unit 1
Tornadoes!

At Home: Have students write a weather report using the vocabulary words.

30a

McGraw-Hill School Division

Story Comprehension

Below are some statements about the information in the article "Tornadoes!"
Write **T** on the line if the statement is true. Write **F** if it is false.

_____ **1.** It takes almost an hour for a twister to form.

_____ **2.** Most tornadoes take place in the spring and summer months.

_____ **3.** Tornadoes usually happen where the land is flat.

_____ **4.** It is impossible to measure the strength of a tornado.

_____ **5.** Tornadoes are not the most powerful storms.

_____ **6.** Tornadoes can sound like a rushing train.

_____ **7.** Radar cannot detect or track tornadoes.

_____ **8.** Scientists know how to stop twisters from forming.

_____ **9.** The color of a tornado depends on the color of the dirt it picks up.

_____ **10.** With new tools, such as computers and satellites, scientists can make

more reliable predictions.

At Home: Have students create a poster that tells about
Tornadoes.

McGraw-Hill School Division

Read a Bibliography

When you write a report, you should include a **bibliography** page that lists the books, magazine articles, and other sources that you used to get your information.

Use the sample bibliography to answer the questions below.

> **Bibliography**
>
> Kelly, Austin. *Famous Tornadoes*. New York: Weather Press, Inc., 1998.
>
> Laporte, Jeanne, ed. *When Disaster Strikes: Essays about Tornadoes, Hurricanes, and Earthquakes.* Washington, D.C.: Quick Reference Publishers, 1999.
>
> Peck, Catherine K. *Tornado: What to Do in an Emergency*. California: Weather Service Press, 1997.
>
> Reyes, Tanner. "Constructing a Tornado Shelter." *The Magazine of Weather* (September, 2000): 35–42.

1. Which of the sources is a magazine article? How do you know? _____

   _____

2. Which source was published in Washington, D.C.? _____

   _____

3. Which source would you look at if you wanted to build a tornado shelter?

   _____

4. Which source would you look at if you wanted to find out what to do when a tornado

   strikes? _____

5. Where would you place this source in the bibliography?

   Genoa, Wendy. *The Weather Source Book*. New York: Weather Press, 1999.

   _____

At Home: Have students write bibliography entries for three of their favorite books or magazines.

McGraw-Hill School Division

Problem and Solution

Characters try to find **solutions** to the **problems** they face in a story. Sometimes characters must try a number of solutions before they find one that solves their problems.

Everybody had come to see the first play of the summer season, a new comedy by a famous author. It was an important night for the theater. The stage lights briefly flickered on, and then the theater went black. Something was wrong with the electrical system. At first the stage manager went into the basement to see if she could fix the problem. But when she flipped the power back on, nothing happened. Then the manager called an electrician, but he said he couldn't come until the next day! Some people in the audience got up to leave. "Wait one moment. We'll work something out," the manager promised. But what would she do?

The actors were all upset. This was their big opportunity. They urged the stage manager to think of something. Suddenly the stage manager had an idea. She asked the audience to go next door to the football field. Above the field were powerful lights. Some people seemed to dislike the idea of watching a play on the football field, so the manager announced, "Ladies and Gentlemen, the show must go on." Everyone applauded. The play was such a success, that from then on they always held the first play of the year on the football field!

Problem	Solution
The power goes out and the stage manager can't fix it.	_____ _____
The audience begins to leave.	_____ _____ _____
The actors urge the stage manager to find a solution.	_____ _____
People were unsure of watching the play from the bleachers.	_____ _____

At Home: Have students write a problem and alternative solutions to the problem.

Book 5/Unit 1
Tornadoes!

4

Synonyms and Antonyms

Synonyms are words with the same or similar meanings. **Antonyms** are words with opposite or nearly opposite meanings.

Compare the pair of underlined words. On the line, write whether the words are more like antonyms or more like synonyms.

1. We heard the <u>tornado</u> watch on the radio and kept an eye out for any dark clouds

   that might form a <u>twister</u>. _____

2. "The cut is not that <u>serious</u>," said the nurse. "It's not a <u>severe</u> wound."

   _____

3. As soon as we saw <u>danger</u> coming, we ran for <u>safety</u>. _____

4. The storm caused so much <u>damage</u>. Have you ever seen such <u>destruction</u>?

   _____

5. I could not <u>detect</u> any trace of evidence. Could it be that it was too well <u>hid</u>?

   _____

6. That weather station has the best <u>predictions</u>. Their <u>forecasts</u> are always right.

   _____

7. He held the <u>top</u>, and I held the <u>bottom</u>. _____

8. That book is <u>reliable</u> as a source of facts, but its opinions are <u>untrustworthy</u>.

   _____

McGraw-Hill School Division

8 Book 5/Unit 1
Tornadoes!

At Home: Have students write more sentences with antonyms and synonyms.

34

Context Clues

You can define an unknown word by using the words surrounding it to give you clues to the word's meaning.

Circle the **context clues** in each sentence that can help you figure out the meaning of the underlined word.

1. <u>Radar</u>, an instrument that uses radio waves, was first used over 50 years ago to locate distant planes and ships.

2. Radar can spot far away aircraft that the eye cannot <u>detect.</u>

3. The telecommunications <u>satellite</u> bounces signals back to Earth from space.

4. <u>Tracking</u> a space shuttle in flight is difficult. It is best to use computers and radar to follow its path.

5. From above the center of the storm we could see its <u>vortex.</u> It was like looking down into a whirlpool.

Use the context clues to fill in the correct vocabulary words from the box.

stadium	reliable	predictions	severe

Because of the _____ storms that hit our area, we decided not to go to the

football _____. Instead, we listened to the most _____ weather

_____ given by the forecasters on the radio.

At Home: Have students define words from the newspaper or a magazine using context clues.

McGraw-Hill School Division

Unit 1 Vocabulary Review

A. Read each word in column 1. Find its antonym, or the word most nearly opposite in meaning, in column 2. Then write the letter of the word on the line.

_____ 1. reluctantly   **a.** necessity

_____ 2. vaguely   **b.** calm

_____ 3. concentrating   **c.** clearly

_____ 4. treacherous   **d.** daydreaming

_____ 5. luxury   **e.** willingly

B. Supply the correct vocabulary word.

banner	convenience	bushel	stadium	hull	shoreline	scroll

6. They were busy building the wooden frame of the ship's _____.

7. The basket was big enough to hold a _____ of wheat.

8. We went to the _____ to watch the track and field events.

9. Can you hang the _____ from the pole?

10. Having a market nearby is a real _____.

11. We walked along the _____, searching for driftwood and seashells.

12. The messenger carefully rolled up the map as if it were a _____.

At Home: Have students write a sentence for each vocabulary word in Part A.

Unit 1 Vocabulary Review

A. Answer each question.

1. **spire**   What does a spire look like? Give an example of a spire.

   _____

2. **timbers**   What are timbers made of? Where can you find them?

   _____

3. **severe**   What is a severe winter storm? What destruction could it cause?

   _____

   _____

4. **approve**   Do you approve of dogs wearing collars?

   _____

B. Write the vocabulary word that means almost the same thing as the underlined word.

predictions	scholarship	detect	ominous	prospered	bruised

5. I <u>injured</u> my elbow when I fell down. _____

6. The almanac has weather <u>forecasts</u> for the entire year. _____

7. She inspected the scene, but could not <u>spot</u> any fingerprints. _____

8. The whole family worked hard and <u>succeeded</u>. _____

9. The storm cloud looked <u>threatening</u>. _____

10. Gina won an <u>award</u> to study at a famous music school. _____

At Home: Have students write a question for each vocabulary word in Part B. Then have them answer the questions. They can use Part A as a guide.

McGraw-Hill School Division

Make Predictions

As you read a story, you probably ask yourself what will happen next. To answer that question, you think about clues in the story and your own experience. Then you make a **prediction,** or guess, about what will happen.

Read each story. Then answer the questions.

The students in Ms. Wang's fifth-grade class are hard workers. They want to do community service projects for their school. For the projects, they can repaint the old fence on the playground, rebuild the broken seesaw, or pull out the weeds in the schoolyard and plant some flowers. Still, the class is not sure which projects they want to do. Although the class has little money to spend on tools, a local hardware store is offering free paint and flower seeds during the month of April. The class will have two weeks in April to do the projects.

1. What projects do you predict the class will do for their community service? _____

_____

2. What story clues helped you make your prediction? _____

_____

3. Will Ms. Wang's class be able to get the work done in time? Why do you think so?

_____

Juanita and Marika are in Juanita's backyard. They are trying to decide what to make for their soccer team's bake sale. Juanita's mother comes out to pick some pears from the tree.

"Taste these pears, girls," she says. "They're delicious. They're perfect for making a pie."

Juanita and Marika each take a bite and then turn to each other and smile. Their dilemma is solved.

4. What do you predict the two girls will make for the soccer team's bake sale? _____

_____

5. What story clues helped you make your prediction? _____

_____

_____

At Home: Have students predict what will happen on a favorite television show. Then have them check their prediction by watching the show.

McGraw-Hill School Division

Vocabulary

Choose the correct word from the box. Then write the word on the line.

shriveled	speechless	stifling	insistent	distressed	despair

1. Riding a bike on a hot day can be a _____ experience.

2. Even though they lost the game, the coach told them not to _____.

3. A _____ face shows sadness.

4. To be _____ is to be at a loss for words.

5. David was so _____ that I went to the movie with him.

6. Dried fruits are _____ and chewy.

At Home: Have students use each of the vocabulary words in a sentence providing clue(s) to the word's meaning.

Book 5/Unit 2
The Gold Coin 6

McGraw-Hill School Division

A Day at the Races

The weather that day was *stifling*. It was too hot and muggy. Our coach was *insistent* that we drink plenty of water. Right before the relay race, Suki, our fastest runner, looked a little *distressed*. She was worried that she might let the team down.

We were doing well in the relay race until I dropped the baton. I felt so awful—as if I had *shriveled* up inside. I could barely move. *Despair* froze my body.

Snatching the baton up from the ground, Suki took off. She flew around that last lap. Suki won the race for us. Later, she came up to me. I wanted to say something, but I was *speechless*. "You ran well," she said kindly.

1. How does it feel when the weather is hot and muggy? _____

2. How does the coach's demanding voice sound? _____

3. How does the fastest runner look? _____

4. What does the narrator feel when she drops the baton? _____

5. Why did the story narrator feel *shriveled* up inside and then *speechless*? _____

_____

_____

At Home: Have students use the vocabulary words to write about a time when they found themselves either speechless or distressed.

Story Comprehension

In the left column are causes for events in "The Gold Coin." In the right column are the effects of those causes. Next to each cause, write the letter of its effect.

	Cause		**Effect**
_____	1. Juan has no friends or family	**a.**	Juan helps them work in the field.
_____	2. Juan steals at night.	**b.**	Juan's body is shriveled and bent.
_____	3. Juan hides and sneaks about.	**c.**	Juan offers to repair her house.
_____	4. Doña Josefa leaves her home.		
_____	5. Father and son must finish digging up potatoes before they give Juan a ride.	**d.**	His face is always twisted into a frown.
		e.	Juan enters the empty hut looking for gold.
_____	6. Juan enjoys home-cooked stew and bread.	**f.**	He thinks of other meals.
_____	7. The girl shows him a family of rabbits.	**g.**	His skin is pale and sickly.
		h.	Juan smiles.
_____	8. Doña Josefa can't leave her house because the roof is damaged and a storm is approaching.		

At Home: Have students write one other sentence identifying cause-and-effect for an event from "The Gold Coin."

McGraw-Hill School Division

Use a Dictionary

---

lum·bar (lum´ bər) *adj.* located in the lower part of the back

lum·ber¹ (lum´ bər) *n.* timber sawed into boards, planks, of standard length; *They bought lumber to build a new house.*

lum·ber² (lum´ bər) *vb.* lum·bered, lum·ber·ing, lum·bers **1.** to cut down (trees) and prepare as marketable timber **2.** to cut down the timber of: *They lumbered the forest until it was gone.*

lum·ber³ (lum´ bər) *vb.* lum·bered, lum·ber·ing, lum·bers **1.** to walk or move with heavy clumsiness; *The sleepy bear lumbered out of the den.* **2.** to move with a rumbling noise

lum·ber·jack (lum´ bər jak´) *n.* someone who fells trees and transports the timber to a mill; a logger

---

Use the sample dictionary page to answer each question.

1. How many entries does the dictionary have for the word *lumber*? _____

2. How many of those entries are verbs? _____

3. How many definitions are listed in each entry for *lumber* as a verb? _____

4. Which entry defines the meaning of *lumber* as it is used in the story? _____

_____

5. How do you know? _____

_____

6. What part of speech is *lumber* used as in the story selection? _____

7. Which definition of lumber is used in this sentence: *The carpenter carefully cut the*

lumber. _____

8. What part of speech is lumber as it is used in the sentence in question 7? _____

At Home: Have students find a word in the dictionary that has more than one definition. Have them write down the different definitions in their own words.

Make Predictions

As you read a story, you can often **make predictions** about what is going to happen. You can do this because the story has clues about the characters and what they are likely to do.

Listed below are some story events from "The Gold Coin." For each one, write a prediction about what will happen next.

1. What character trait of Juan helped you predict that he would force open the window and climb into Doña Josefa's empty hut looking for gold? _____

   _____

2. What previous event helped you predict that Juan would help the young man pick corn? _____

3. What events in the story would help you predict that Juan might stop being a thief and a loner? _____

   _____

4. What character clues helped you predict that Doña Josefa was not a woman rich in gold? _____

   _____

5. What new character trait of Juan helped you predict that he will help rebuild Doña Josefa's house? _____

   _____

At Home: Ask students to predict what might have happened in each family if Doña Josefa had not visited them.

42

Book 5/Unit 2
The Gold Coin 5

Form Generalizations

A **generalization** is a broad statement based on convincing examples. Juan is an example of a man who learns the importance of helping others. Answer each question about Juan. Look back through the selection if you need to. Then use your answers to form a generalization about helping others.

1. Why, at first, does Juan help people with their crops in the fields? _____

_____

_____

2. What generalization would describe what Juan feels when he's helping people in

their fields? _____

_____

3. Make a generalization about how Juan learns a lesson from other people. What

does he learn? _____

_____

_____

4. Make a generalization about how Juan's character changes by the end of the story.

_____

_____

5. Based on the example of Juan, make a generalization about the importance of

helping others. _____

_____

5 Book 5/Unit 2
The Gold Coin

At Home: Ask students to make another generalization from the story. Have them write down two examples that support the statement: one from the story, the other from real life.

43

Compound Words

You can figure out the meaning of a compound word by looking at the two base words and putting the two meanings together.

A **closed** compound has two words written together as one word. An **open** compound has two words written separately or separated by a hyphen, such as home-cooked.

Below are clues or definitions for some compound words. Complete the chart.

Definition	Compound Word	Base Word
1. some person	_____	_____ + _____
2. traveling on the back of a horse	_____	_____ + _____
3. when the sun goes down	_____	_____ + _____
4. meals cooked at home	_____	_____ + _____
5. a kitchen cabinet for storing cups and plates	_____	_____ + _____
6. the opposite of hello	_____	_____ + _____

Combine a word from the first column with one from the second column to form six closed compound words from the "The Gold Coin." Write the words on each line provided.

7. sugar   hills   _____

8. new   bank   _____

9. river   light   _____

10. day   side   _____

11. foot   cane   _____

12. hill   born   _____

At Home: Ask students to find four other compound words from words in "The Gold Coin."

McGraw-Hill School Division

Fact and Nonfact

A **fact** is a statement or idea that can be proven to be true. A **nonfact** is something that is made up and can be proven to be false. In a story, nonfacts can be exaggerations of a character's behavior or abilities.

Read the story. Then decide whether each sentence is a fact or nonfact. Explain the reason for your decision.

George Washington was the first President of the United States. He was a tall man. It's hard to believe but Washington was over nine feet tall. It is commonly believed that his favorite food was cherry pie. When George was only 9-years-old he ate 50 cherry pies at a time without getting sick. When he was older he decided to plant cherry trees at his home in Mount Vernon, Virginia. Later, he planted cherry trees all over Washington, D.C.

Story Statement	Fact or Nonfact	Explanation
1. George Washington was the first President of the United States.	_____	_____ _____ _____
2. It's hard to believe but Washington was over nine feet tall.	_____	_____ _____ _____
3. He ate 50 pies.	_____	_____ _____ _____ _____ _____ _____
4. His home was in Mount Vernon, Virginia	_____	_____ _____
5. He planted cherry trees at his home in Mount Vernon	_____	_____ _____

At Home: Have students take 2 of their favorite stories and tell what parts could be factual and what parts are obviously nonfact.

Vocabulary

For each sentence below, supply the correct word from the box.

acre	commotion	dynamite	grit	pulverized	rebuild

1. After the flood, we had to _____ the town on higher ground.

2. They used _____ to blast away what was left of the old sea wall.

3. It was amazing to see how the blast _____ huge rocks into dust.

4. It was such a windy day at the beach that we could taste _____ every time we bit into a sandwich.

5. Many people wanted to provide at least one _____ of green space for a downtown park.

6. When protesting the new rule banning dogs from the park, the angry crowd caused a _____.

Growing Pains

Deep in the heart of the city, nestled among the tall skyscrapers, there was a very small, old house, built on a huge rock.

Some people wanted to tear down the old house and replace it with a big, modern office building. This idea caused a lot of *commotion*. People all over town protested because they liked the little, old house. The house was special. Finally, someone suggested that they could move the house and *rebuild* it on an *acre* of land outside of town. The land was lush and green and the perfect setting for the house. Everyone agreed that that was a good idea, so they moved the house.

After they moved the house, they had to remove the huge rock. They *pulverized* the rock with *dynamite*. Soon all that was left of the rock was gravel, *grit*, and dust, and space to build the modern office building.

1. Why did the idea of taking down the house cause a lot of *commotion?* _____

_____

2. How did the people decide to solve the problem of the little, old house? _____

_____

3. Where did they move the house to? _____

_____

4. What was used to *pulverize* a huge rock? _____

5. What is smaller, a rock or a piece of *grit*? _____

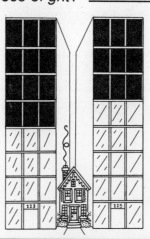

At Home: Have students use the vocabulary words to write about how they would have solved the problem of the old house.

Story Comprehension

Answer these questions about "John Henry." Look back at the story if you need help.

1. Why did John Henry and his father need to rebuild the porch? _____

_____

2. Who was Ferret-Faced Freddy? _____

3. What sort of bet did John Henry make with Ferret-Faced Freddy? _____

_____

4. What did John Henry's father give him when John left his family? _____

_____

5. What could John Henry do with his sledgehammers that dynamite could not? _____

_____

6. What would wrap around John Henry's shoulders as he worked with his

sledgehammers? _____

7. What was the last big job John Henry did in his life? _____

_____

8. Is "John Henry" a true story. How do you know? _____

_____

_____

At Home: Have students write down three events from the
story and explain how those events describe John Henry.

Use the Internet

You can use the **Internet** to search for information you need. For instance, the page below is a search for toymakers.

Use the Internet entries below to answer the questions.

British Toymakers Guild
Founded in 1955 to promote good original design and craftsmanship in toymaking.
http://www.toy.co.uk/associations/btg.html

Mexican Toymakers
Pinatas and rattles are displayed and instructions on how to make them are available.
http://www.utexas.edu/depts/tmm/exhibits/Toy/index.html

The Toymakers Speak
Below is an interview with the one of the STW Toys Space Nine Galaxy members. Look for monthly interviews with different team members that will answer questions from the people who ACTUALLY make the toys.
http://spacenine.STW.com/low/model/interview.html

---

1. How many web pages did the search engine find for "toymakers"? _____

2. How many of these entries are about toys or toymakers in other countries? _____

3. Which website seems to offer the most information about people who make toys?

   Explain. _____

4. What key words would you type into the search engine if you wanted to find out more

   about the people who make a specific toy? _____

   _____

5. If you wanted to go to the website on Mexican toymakers, how could you get there

   from this screen? _____

   _____

---

5 Book 5/Unit 2
John Henry

At Home: Have students write out a list of Internet research topics of interest.

48

Fact and Nonfact

Legends can include **facts** and **nonfacts**. Some story events might be real, but the writer often creates and includes other events that are not real. Those events are nonfacts.

Below are some story events from "John Henry." If you think the event could be based on fact or proven true, write **Fact**. If you think the event could be proven false or that it was made up write **Nonfact**, and explain why.

_____ **1.** When John Henry was born, a unicorn came to see him.

_____

_____ **2.** John Henry grew fast. _____

_____ **3.** As a baby, John Henry grew so fast he busted through the porch.

_____

_____ **4.** In less than half a day John Henry could clear an acre of trees

and chop them into firewood. _____

_____

_____ **5.** John Henry challenged Ferret-Faced Freddy to a race. John ran,

while Freddy rode his horse. _____

_____ **6.** When John Henry raced Ferret-Faced Freddy, he ran so fast that

you couldn't see him. _____

_____ **7.** John Henry was stronger than dynamite. _____

_____

_____ **8.** John Henry could beat a steam drill.

_____

_____

At Home: Have students find other story events in "John Henry" that must be nonfacts, even if they are based on real events. Ask them to tell how they know they are nonfacts.

Book 5/Unit 2
John Henry 8

McGraw-Hill School Division

Form Generalizations

A **generalization** is a broad statement, or rule, that in many instances is true. To show that a generalization is usually **valid**, or true, you must be able to give several examples to support it. A generalization could be **faulty** if you can find an instance where the statement does not apply.

For each generalization write in the chart one example from your life experience that supports the statement and another example that proves it is faulty. Then write whether you think the generalization is still valid. Explain your answer.

Generalization: All birds fly south in the winter.

example: proves it's valid	example: proves it's faulty
1. _____ _____	2. _____ _____

Generalization: Websites on the Internet have useful information.

example: proves it's valid	example: proves it's faulty
3. _____ _____	4. _____ _____

Generalization: Pets have four legs and a tail.

example: proves it's valid	example: proves it's faulty
5. _____ _____	6. _____ _____

At Home: Ask students to look for generalizations while they read. Then have them explain if the generalization is valid or faulty.

50

McGraw-Hill School Division

Inflectional Endings

You can change many adjectives to the **comparative** form by adding *–er* or *–ier*. These endings are called **inflectional endings**. You can change many adjectives to the superlative form by adding the *–est* or *–iest* inflectional endings.

Examples are:
Loud + er = louder
Loud + est = loudest
Often there are spelling changes when you add *–ier* and *–iest*.
Examples:
merry + *–ier* = merrier
merry + *–iest* = merriest

A legend like "John Henry" uses a lot of exaggeration. Many adjectives are used to make comparisons and to describe characters and events.

Use inflectional endings to complete the base, or positive form, of each adjective in the chart below.

	Positive	Comparative	Superlative
1.	big	_____	_____
2.	fast	_____	_____
3.	pretty	_____	_____
4.	funny	_____	_____
5.	mean	_____	_____
6.	nice	_____	_____

For each sentence, choose the correct adjective form and write it on the line.

7. Kira is the _____ girl on the team.   (tall, taller, tallest)

8. Sonny can be so _____ sometimes. (kind, kinder, kindest)

9. That was the _____ test I ever took. (hard, harder, hardest)

10. This computer is _____ than yours. (slow, slower, slowest)

At Home: Ask students to think of four other adjectives that can take the inflectional endings *–er/–ier* and *–est/ –iest* and create a chart like the one above.

51

Book 5/Unit 2
John Henry   10

McGraw-Hill School Division

Main Idea

Writers sometimes organize information in a story according to the **main idea** or the major, or most important, point of a story. **Supporting details** are details that reinforce the main idea. Read each paragraph. First circle the letter of the sentence you think best states the main idea of the paragraph. Then write down some of the details that support the main idea.

Too many students are coming to school unprepared. Many are late for class or forget their homework. They lose school books. They don't have any pencils. They have no paper. How can they study like this?

1. a. Students should sharpen more pencils and have notebooks to write in.

   b. Too many students are not prepared for school.

2. Supporting details: _____

   _____

There is a way to get more children to read. Children learn to read best when people read to them. Parents need to take the time to read to their children. Even older children can help by reading to younger children.

3. a. Older children should help younger ones to read.

   b. The best way to get children to read is to read to them.

4. Supporting details: _____

   _____

Hiking up mountains is hard work. The last thing you want is a heavy backpack to haul. So, when you are packing, keep it light. Remember, you can't bring everything with you, and you really don't want to.

5. a. Travel light, pack little when hiking.

   b. Don't hike up mountains if you have a heavy backpack.

6. Supporting details: _____

   _____

McGraw-Hill School Division

At Home: Have students identify the main idea in three magazine articles. Encourage them to share any major ideas that interest them.

Vocabulary

For each sentence below, supply the correct vocabulary word from the box.

auction	dangled	deliveries	donate	lecture	publicity

1. The class decided to _____ the money they raised from the car wash to the new public zoo.

2. "Please, don't _____ me about doing the dishes!" she pleaded.

3. No one is going to know about the show, unless there is _____ for it.

4. Akisha admired the colorful earrings that _____ from her aunt's ears.

5. They sold all the old books at an _____ where they hoped to get the most money they could for them.

6. We had so many _____ to make before noon that we left at dawn.

At Home: Have students use each of the vocabulary words in a sentence.

Box 5/Unit 2
It's Our World, Too! 6

McGraw-Hill School Division

Top Bid

The students were raising money to help build homes for homeless people. They were going to have an *auction*. An article in the local newspaper and a radio interview were all the *publicity* the students needed. Everyone in town was willing to *donate* something! Soon *deliveries* were coming, and things were piling up in every corner of the storeroom. Some things even *dangled* from the ceiling!

The best part was that no one had to go around town and *lecture* business owners about doing the right thing. They just did it! Everyone was eager to take part in the auction. When they held the auction, lots of people came and bid on items. Some people even bought back their donations! After all, it was for a good cause.

1. What does *lecture* mean as it is used here? _____.

2. What is another word for *dangled*? _____.

3. How were the students going to raise money? _____.

4. How did the newspaper article and radio interview help the students? _____

_____

5. What did students need people to do to make the auction successful? _____

_____

5 Book 5/Unit 2
It's Our World, Too!

At Home: Have students come up with a plan to help a charity using vocabulary words.

53a

Story Comprehension

Read each list of events for Justin Lebo and Dwaina Brooks. Number the events in each list from 1 to 8 to show the order in which they occurred.

Justin Lebo

_____ Justin gives two bikes to the boys at the Kilbarchan Home.

_____ Justin fixes up two old bikes for fun.

_____ Justin asks his parents for matching dollars to help him buy old bikes for parts.

_____ Justin begins to run out of bikes and money.

_____ Justin builds bikes for kids living in a home for children with AIDS.

_____ Justin decides to make 19 more bikes for the boys.

_____ A reporter writes an article about Justin's project and asks readers to help.

_____ People donate many bikes and money.

Dwaina Brooks

_____ A young homeless man tells Dwaina he would love a really good meal.

_____ Dwaina notices men and women outside a homeless shelter each morning.

_____ Dwaina and her mother carefully shop for food.

_____ Dwaina, her mother, and sisters assemble the meals on Friday nights.

_____ The class sets up an assembly line in the Brooks' kitchen to make more meals.

_____ Dwaina asks her fifth grade class to help put the meals together.

_____ Dwaina asks her mother to help her make meals for the homeless.

_____ Dwaina decides to make more meals for the homeless.

At Home: Have students write about ways that they could use their own skills or interests to help others.

McGraw-Hill School Division

Use a Telephone Directory

Most telephone directories have three parts. The **Blue Pages** list local, state, and federal government services. The **Yellow Pages** list businesses. The **White Pages** list home phone numbers and addresses.

White Pages	Yellow Pages	Blue Pages
SODERBERG, Abby 12 Park Av **555–1766**	**ADAM'S RARE BOOKS** 207 South **555–1955**	**COMMUNITY SERVICES** Codes & Permits 405 Grand Ave **555–5271**
Don & Bonnie 27 Cottonwood **555–7486**	**CHICKERING BOOKSTORE** 203 South **555–8609**	City Planning 405 Grand Av **555–5386**
SOLTERO, Angelina 1321 Steele **555–2660**	**SECOND STORY BOOKS** 105 Ivinson **555–4423**	Parks & Recreation 405 Grand Av **555–2067**
Gavino 820 South Pine **555–4952**		
SONI, Bunit 265 North 7 . . . .**555–1129**		

Use the sample sections from the telephone directories to answer these questions.

1. If you are looking for the home phone number of a friend, where do you look?

   _____.

2. What number would you call to reach Gavino Soltero on South Pine St.?

   _____.

3. What telephone directory would you use to find out about community services?

   _____.

4. Which number would you call to find out about local parks?

   _____.

5. What telephone directory would you use to find listings of bookstores?

   _____.

6. Which number would you call to ask about a rare book?

   _____.

At Home: Have students study the information provided in the front pages of their local telephone directories. Ask them to list some of the new things they discovered there.

Main Idea

First answer the questions about the **main idea** for each section from "It's Our World, Too!" Then use **supporting details** from "It's Our World, Too!" to fill in the story chart below.

Which of the following statements do you think best reflects the major message that Justin sends in "It's Our World, Too!"? Circle the letter.

1. a. We should recycle and fix all old bikes for people who can't afford them.

   b. If you want to help others, do something that makes you happy at the same time.

   c. Wheels mean freedom. That's why every boy and girl should have a bike.

Which of the following statements do you think best reflects the major message that Dwaina sends in "It's Our World, Too!"? Circle the letter.

2. a. You should help others because each of us has been helped by someone.

   b. The only way to help the homeless is to make them home-cooked meals.

   c. If people aren't helping each other, you need to lecture them.

Story Chart

	Justin Lebo	Dwaina Brooks
Skills	3. _____ _____	4. _____ _____
What they did	5. _____ _____ _____ _____	6. _____ _____ _____ _____
Whom they helped	7. _____ _____ _____ _____	8. _____ _____ _____ _____
Who helped them	9. _____ _____ _____ _____	10. _____ _____ _____ _____

At Home: Encourage students to identify the main idea and supporting details on a television news program or talk show.

Book 5/Unit 2
It's Our World, Too!

10

McGraw-Hill School Division

Fact and Nonfact

A statement or an idea that can be proved true is a **fact**. A statement or an idea that can be proved false, is a **nonfact**.

Read each statement and decide whether it is a fact or a nonfact. Write **Fact** if it is a fact and **Nonfact** if it is a nonfact.

_____ **1.** The sun rises in the east in the morning and sets in the west in the evening.

_____ **2.** The blue whale's skin is colored green.

_____ **3.** You need special equipment to breathe on the moon.

_____ **4.** There are rain forests on the moon.

_____ **5.** Only people who drive red cars are caught speeding.

_____ **6.** The Japanese bullet train travels faster than our local trains.

_____ **7.** Sea water tastes salty.

_____ **8.** A rain cloud actually feels like a giant, fluffy cotton ball.

McGraw-Hill School Division

At Home: Have students make a list of facts and nonfacts that interest them. They can then ask a friend or family member to distinguish the facts from the nonfacts.

Inflectional Endings

You can change many adjectives to the comparative form by adding the **inflectional endings** –er. You can change many adjectives to the superlative form by adding –est.

Some adjectives, however, take an irregular form in the comparative and superlative. For example, the adjective *many* is *more* in the comparative and *most* in the superlative.

Complete the adjective chart below.

Adjective	Comparative	Superlative
1. many	more	most
2. bad	_____	_____
3. well	_____	_____
4. little	_____	_____
5. much	_____	_____
6. good	_____	_____
7. late	_____	_____
8. far	_____	_____
9. cold	_____	_____

For each sentence, write the correct form of the underlined word.

10. This bicycle is <u>brokener</u> than that one. _____

11. There are <u>badder</u> ways to get a flat tire. _____

12. He is the <u>unusualest</u> teacher in the school. _____

13. You have to be <u>carefuller</u> about these things. _____

At Home: Ask students to choose two adjectives from the chart. Then, for each adjective, have them write a sentence showing each degree of comparison. They can refer to this chart for help.

Book 5/Unit 2 /12
It's Our World, Too!

McGraw-Hill School Division

Make Predictions

A **prediction** is a guess based on knowledge. You can make predictions about characters and story events by using story clues and your own experience to guess what will happen next in the story.

Read each story. Then answer the questions.

Dawn was breaking over the lake as Antonio snuck down to the dock. It was a perfect day to take one of the sailboats out on the lake. Finally he could sail by himself. Antonio set sail, ignoring the sign on the dock that stated: "No sailing without permission. No sailing alone." Things were perfect, until huge waves started rocking the boat. Looking up, Antonio saw another sailboat coming straight at him. His fingers froze on the rudder.

1. What do you predict will happen next? _____

_____

2. What story clues most helped you make your prediction? _____

_____

3. What do you predict Antonio will do next? _____

_____

Jasmine was helping Hu transplant flowers to his mother's flower garden. It was their first time transplanting flowers. Digging the holes was hard work, so they decided not to dig deep holes so the work would go faster. Suddenly the sky filled with ominous, dark clouds. Big rain drops started to fall just as they finished planting the last row. The children hurried inside to tell Hu's mother that the garden was planted. His mother looked out the window at the heavy rain, saw the flowers sticking out of the small holes, and sighed.

4. What do you predict might happen to the newly planted flowers? _____

_____

5. What story clues helped you make your prediction? Explain. _____

_____

_____

5 Book 5/Unit 2
Dear Mr. Henshaw

At Home: Ask students to make predictions as they watch a cartoon or a film. Have them write their predictions and then revise or change them after they have watched the entire cartoon or film.

59

Vocabulary

Rewrite this paragraph. Replace the underlined words and phrases with the following vocabulary words.

afford	permission	rejected	reserved	snoop	submitted

Today was not Tamika's best day. When she went to the library to pick up a book that had been set aside _____ for her, she found that someone else had checked it out. Tamika needed the book to write a report, and she could not spare the money _____ to buy it. When she got home there was a letter in the mailbox from a magazine. She knew it was about the story that she had sent in _____ months ago. The story was a humorous one about a retired neighbor who everyone thought was a nosy person _____, but was really a smart detective. Tamika sighed. She was afraid that the magazine was probably telling her that they had turned down _____ her work. To her delight, however, the letter was from the editor asking for consent _____ to print the story in their next issue! Maybe today would turn out okay after all!

McGraw-Hill School Division

Quick Take

"You *snoop*! What are you doing in my room?" said Cali. "You know you aren't supposed to be in here without my *permission*."

"I am not going through your things. I just need to borrow the camera," said Abdul, feeling a little *rejected* by his older sister's response.

"Well, take the camera, and leave!" said Cali.

"Look, I know that I shouldn't be in your room, but the camera does belong to the whole family," muttered Abdul. Then in a louder voice, he said, "It is not *reserved* for just you, Cali. Besides, I can't *afford* to get my own camera right now. And I need it to reshoot some things for the article I *submitted* last week to the school paper."

1. What vocabulary word means to be turned down or turned away? _____

   _____

2. Why do you think Cali wants Abdul to ask permission to enter her room? _____

   _____

3. What vocabulary word describes someone who tries to find out about your business

   in a sneaky way? _____

4. Why does Abdul need to borrow the camera? _____

   _____

   _____

5. Why might Abdul feel that Cali thinks the camera has been reserved just for her?

   _____

   _____

McGraw-Hill School Division

5 Book 5/Unit 2
   Dear Mr. Henshaw

At Home: Have students write a short essay about privacy using the vocabulary words.

60a

Story Comprehension

Write a brief summary of Leigh's diary entry for each date below.

1. Tuesday, March 20

_____

_____

_____

_____

2. Saturday, March 24

_____

_____

_____

_____

3. Sunday, March 25

_____

_____

_____

_____

4. Monday, March 26

_____

_____

_____

_____

5. Friday, March 30

_____

_____

_____

_____

At Home: Have students write a short narrative of their
week's events in diary form.

McGraw-Hill School Division

Use an Encyclopedia Index

Dolphin (sea animal) **D: 296** *with pictures*	**Dolphin figure**
	Swimming (Synchronized swimming) **S:1047-1048**
See also River dolphin *in this index*	
	Dolphin kick
Killer whale **K:316**	
	Swimming (basic kicks) **S:1043**
Mammal, *pictures on* **M:117**	
	Dolphins, Miami
Porpoise **P:679**	
	Football (National Football League) **F:36**
Tuna **T:485**	
Whale (Dolphins and porpoises) **W:258**	
Zoo (facts about zoo animals) **Z:605**	

Use the sample **encyclopedia index** to answer each question.

1. How many volumes contain information about dolphins, the sea animal? _____

2. Where would you look to find an article on the dolphin kick? _____

3. On which page does the encyclopedia article about killer whales begin? _____

4. Does the first article about dolphins show pictures? How do you know? _____

_____

5. Why is it sometimes best to check the index first when researching a topic in an

encyclopedia? _____

_____

_____

5 Book 5/Unit 2
Dear Mr. Henshaw

At Home: Have students use an encyclopedia index to see how many articles they can find about a favorite subject.

62

Make Predictions

As you read a story, you can **make predictions** about what might happen next. The story contains clues about what characters are likely to do.

Read the story events from "Dear Mr. Henshaw." For each one, what did you predict the characters might do.

1. Miss Neely tells Leigh that he still has 24 hours to submit a story to the Young Writers' Yearbook contest. _____

   _____

2. The night that Barry gets invited to dinner, Leigh's mother cooks a casserole full of good things. _____

   _____

3. Leigh gets up his courage to ask his mom if she thinks his dad would remarry.

   _____

   _____

4. Leigh receives an Honorable Mention for his story, "A Day on Dad's Rig." _____

   _____

   _____

5. Leigh finds out that the mysterious Famous Author is Angela Badger. _____

   _____

   _____

   _____

6. It turns out that the winning poem was not original, so Leigh is asked if he would like to go to the lunch with Angela Badger and the other winners. _____

   _____

   _____

7. Miss Neely calls Leigh's mother to ask her permission for Leigh to go to the lunch.

   _____

   _____

8. Angela Badger tells the students that they shouldn't try to write like someone else.

   _____

   _____

At Home: Have students make predictions about their current reading.

McGraw-Hill School Division

Form Generalizations

A **generalization** is a broad statement, or rule, that is true in many instances.

Form a generalization for each of the two statements below.

1. I never see bears in the winter months. Bears sleep when it is cold. _____
_____

2. In the Midwest, dangerous twisters occur suddenly. They happen during spring and
summer. _____
_____
_____

3. I read an article about pets. It said 3 out of 5 people own a cat. _____
_____

4. Arabian horses are very fast. Arabian horses are usually black. _____
_____

5. On hot days we go to the beach. The water is cool and refreshing. _____
_____

6. The panda is an adorable animal. It is very popular at the zoo. _____
_____

7. Fruit is good for you. We eat healthy breakfasts. _____
_____

8. Sharks were spotted at a local beach. Swimming in shark-infested waters is
dangerous. _____
_____

8   Book 5/Unit 2
Dear Mr. Henshaw   **At Home:** Ask students to form two generalizations about
their day-to-day habits.   **64**

Compound Words

You can figure out the meaning of a **compound word** by looking at the two smaller words within it and putting the two meanings together. Words that are formed by joining two smaller words are called closed compound words.

Below are clues or definitions for compound words used in "Dear Mr. Henshaw." Complete the chart.

Definition	Compound Word	Two Words
1. a box for carrying your lunch	_____	_____ + _____
2. a book published at the end of the school year	_____	_____ + _____
3. a basket to put waste in	_____	_____ + _____
4. someone who looks to see if anyone is coming	_____	_____ + _____
5. to shift into a lower gear	_____	_____ + _____
6. the machine that writers used to use to type	_____	_____ + _____

Sometimes a compound word is made up of two words separated by a space or by a hyphen. This is called an open compound word.

Examples are *hot cakes* and *take-out*.

Match the words in each column to make open compound words. Then write the words on the lines provided.

7. salad   cream   _____

8. ice   bar   _____

At Home: Have students make lists of other compound words and tell whether they are open or closed.

Book 5/Unit 2
Dear Mr. Henshaw 10

Main Idea

Writers sometimes organize information in a story according to the **main idea** and supporting details. A main idea is the major, or most important, point that a writer makes. **Supporting details** are details that reinforce the main idea. Read each passage, and then list the main idea and supporting details.

In order to be healthy, you must eat right and stay active. Eating too much sugar and fat can lead to health problems. Avoid junk food. Eat plenty of fruits and vegetables. Take time out each day to exercise.

1. Main Idea: _____

2. Supporting details: _____
   _____
   _____

Have you noticed how supermarkets are organized? They have a common pattern. Fruits and vegetables are in the same section in or near the front. The meat and deli section is usually against a back wall. Milk, eggs, and cheese are near the produce section. The frozen foods are often in refrigerated areas in the middle of the store. The shelved areas are organized by product, such as pasta, rice, and beans in one aisle, and soups, canned vegetables, and fruits in another aisle. As a result things are easy to find in a supermarket.

3. Main Idea: _____

4. Supporting details: _____
   _____

Helen Keller was an inspiring person. A childhood illness left Helen deaf and blind. Life for Helen Keller was not easy because most people at that time felt there was nothing that could be done to help her. But with the guidance of her teacher, Annie Sullivan, Helen learned to read, write, and speak. She graduated from college with honors. Giving speeches and writing best selling books, Helen proved that all people could succeed.

5. Main Idea: _____
   _____

6. Supporting details: _____
   _____

6 Book 5/Unit 2
Digging up the Past

At Home: Have students identify the main idea and supporting details of a newspaper.

66

Vocabulary

Complete each sentence with a word from the box.

arrowheads	bullet	eventually	fraction	starvation	violent

1. The museum had a Civil War rifle, but not a single _____ to go with it.

2. It was such a snowy day that only a _____ of the class could make it to school.

3. We decided to write about the three_____ we found while walking through a forest.

4. There is no reason why people in our town should go without food or die from

   _____ .

5. It was such a _____ storm that the wind knocked down many trees and power lines.

6. It took a while, but _____ we were able to finish our project.

At Home: Have students use each of the vocabulary words in a sentence.

Book 5/Unit 2
Digging Up the Past
6

McGraw-Hill School Division

Forest Findings

Rosita and Kiang liked to collect interesting things. One day they spent the morning in the forest searching for *arrowheads.*

"I would rather find one of these than a *bullet,*" said Kiang.

"I agree. Bows and arrows seem less *violent,*" said Rosita. "Also, I feel bows and arrows come from an older time in history. Let's see what we have so far."

They counted out a dozen. A *fraction* of them were made from a black, glassy rock. *Eventually* they collected 15 more arrowheads.

"Let's head back to my house for lunch," suggested Kiang. "It's way past lunch time.

"Good idea! I'm so hungry I might die of *starvation,*" laughed Rosita.

1. What are Kiang and Rosita searching for? _____

2. What do they think is more violent than bows and arrows? _____

3. What does fraction mean as it is used in this story? _____

_____

4. What words could you use to replace *eventually* in this story? _____

_____

5. What do you think Kiang and Rosita will do with the *arrowheads?* _____

_____

At Home: Encourage students to talk about things that they find interesting and like to collect.

Story Comprehension

Below are some statements about "Digging Up the Past."

Based on the information you read in the article, write **T** on the line if the statement is true, write **F** if it is false.

_____ 1. Jamestown, Virginia, was the first permanent English settlement in North America.

_____ 2. The skeleton the archaeologists found was nearly 700 years old.

_____ 3. Nothing was left of the old fort. Everything had been washed away by the James River.

_____ 4. The first English ship arrived in what is today Virginia in 1607 carrying men, women, and children.

_____ 5. The English colonists named the settlement after King James of Britain.

_____ 6. The Jamestown colonists built a triangle-shaped fort along the river.

_____ 7. The colonists built the fort to protect themselves from attacking bears.

_____ 8. In 1698, a flood destroyed the buildings in Jamestown.

_____ 9. The archaeologists found old toys buried at the Jamestown site.

_____ 10. Archaeologists have explored only a fraction of the fort's grounds so far.

McGraw-Hill School Division

Conduct an Interview

An **interview** is a way to gain information from someone. An interview follows a pattern of questions and answers. To prepare yourself to interview somebody, you need to figure out what questions you should ask.

Think about how you would conduct an interview with someone. Then answer the questions below.

1. Why is it important to know something about the person you are going to interview

   before you conduct the interview? _____

   _____

2. Why should you write down the questions you want to ask? _____

   _____

   _____

3. Why do you need to take notes during the interview? _____

   _____

4. Why is it important to be polite during the interview? _____

   _____

   _____

5. What sort of information does an interview give that you might not find in a book or

   another reference source? _____

   _____

   _____

5   Book 5/Unit 2
Digging Up the Past

At Home: Write five questions you would ask if you were interviewing a reporter about what his or her job is like.

69

Form Generalizations

A **generalization** is a broad statement about a topic. Use what you learned in "Digging Up the Past" to complete the generalizations below.

1. Like most early settlements, Jamestown was named for _____
   _____

2. Early settlers were almost always _____

3. The fort built by the settlers was _____

4. The soil and climate of Virginia seemed _____

5. Early settlers often died of _____
   _____

6. All archaeologists don't dig things up; they _____

7. Overall, artifacts, such as pistols, knives, and armor, tell _____

8. Jamestown was settled over _____

9. Archaeologists try to answer _____

10. Often stories about people like Pocahontas are _____

At Home: Ask students to form one more generalization
from "Digging Up the Past."

Book 5/Unit 2
Digging Up the Past 10

McGraw-Hill School Division

Compound Words

You can figure out the meaning of each **compound word** by looking at the two smaller words within it and putting the two meanings together.

Complete the chart using the clues or definitions below to form compound words from "Digging Up the Past."

Definition	Compound Word	Two Words
1. sticks for holding candles	_____	_____ + _____
2. what you put at the head of an arrow	_____	_____ + _____
3. the town named after King James	_____	_____ + _____
4. a barbed hook for catching fish	_____	_____ + _____
5. below the ground	_____	_____ + _____

Match the words in each column to make compound words, then write the four compound words on the lines provided.

6. home   work   _____

7. foot   head   _____

8. along   wood   _____

9. fire   step   _____

10. fore   side   _____

10 Book 5/Unit 2
Digging Up the Past

At Home: Have students write compound words for things that they use each day.

71

Inflectional Endings

You can create verbs in the past tense by adding the **inflectional endings** *–ed* or *–ing*.

For example: <u>walk</u>   They <u>walked</u> home.   I <u>was walking</u> to the train station.

You can change many adjectives to the superlative form by adding *–est*.

For example: <u>tall</u> She was the <u>tallest</u> girl in class.

It is important to note that there may be spelling changes when *–est* is added.

For example: <u>Busy</u> The holidays are the store's *busiest* time of year.

Rewrite each sentence below using the past tense form of the verb in parentheses.

1. We (walk) into town. _____

2. The ships (sail) across the sea. _____

3. I was (wonder) what dolphins dream about. _____

   _____

4. The cowboy (hitch) his horse to the post. _____

   _____

5. Colorful kites were (soar) in the sky. _____

6. That team (trade) my favorite player. _____

Rewrite each sentence below using the superlative form of the adjective in parentheses.

7. This puzzle is the (hard) of all. _____

8. That would be the (wise) thing to do. _____

9. In the summer, the attic is the (hot) room. _____

10. We saw the (funny) magic show. _____

At Home: Have students write sentences using four verbs that use the inflectional endings -ed and -ing.

McGraw-Hill School Division

Unit 2 Vocabulary Review

1. Read each word in column 1. Find its antonym, or the word most nearly opposite in meaning, in column 2. Then write the letter of the antonym on the line.

_____	**1.** rejected	**a.** peaceful
_____	**2.** violent	**b.** hope
_____	**3.** despair	**c.** wanted
_____	**4.** commotion	**d.** secrecy
_____	**5.** publicity	**e.** calm

B. Supply the correct vocabulary word.

afford	bullet	deliveries	distressed	dynamite	shriveled	snoop

1. Who was the _____ sneaking around in my room?

2. I have an early morning job making newspaper _____.

3. The road crew used _____ to blast through the mountain rock.

4. They could not _____ to buy the fancy bike.

5. The doctor quickly removed a _____ from the soldier's arm.

6. Some people get _____ when they have to take tests.

7. Annie found _____ dried up flowers on the windowsill.

Book 5/Unit 2
Unit 2 Vocabulary Review
12

At Home: Have students write a sentence for each vocabulary word in Part A.

73

McGraw-Hill School Division

Unit 2 Vocabulary Review

A. Answer each question.

1. **auction**   What sort of things would you find at an auction?

   _____

2. **grit**   What does grit feel like?

   _____

3. **stifling**   When is a room stifling?

   _____

4. **permission**   What do you need permission to do?

   _____

B. Write the vocabulary word that means almost the same thing as the underlined word or words.

donate	lecture	fraction	insistent	pulverized	starvation

1. My parents <u>give money</u> each year to the animal shelter. _____

2. When there isn't enough food, some animals die of <u>hunger</u>. _____

3. He was so <u>demanding</u> that I did what he told me to do. _____

4. We ate a <u>small portion</u> of the pumpkin pie. _____

5. Please don't <u>scold</u> me about doing homework. _____

6. The giant machine <u>crushed</u> the concrete slabs. _____

At Home: Have students write a question for each vocabulary word in Part B. Then have them answer the questions. They can use Part A as a guide.

74

Book 5/Unit 2
Unit 2 Vocabulary Review   /10

McGraw-Hill School Division

Steps in a Process

A series of steps that you follow in order are **steps in a process.**

Each of the following activities has several steps that need to be followed in order. Write numbers 1 through 4 on the lines to show the right order.

Give a Speech

_____ Create note cards with keywords on the topic.

_____ Research a topic.

_____ Practice giving your speech.

_____ Decide on a topic.

Write a Book Report

_____ Write the book report.

_____ Read the book.

_____ Choose a book for the report.

_____ Make a cover for the book report.

Plan a Surprise party

_____ Send out invitations.

_____ Greet the guest of honor by jumping out and yelling "Surprise!"

_____ Choose a day for the party.

_____ Hide until the guest of honor arrives.

Direct a Play

_____ Admit people to the show on opening night

_____ Choose a play to present.

_____ Audition actors.

_____ Direct actors as they rehearse scenes and choose costumes.

16 Book 5/Unit 3
The Marble Champ

At Home: Have students identify a step-by-step process that they follow at home. Have them write the steps in order.

75

Vocabulary

Choose a vocabulary word to complete the sentence. Then answer the question using the vocabulary word.

| accurate | division | onlookers | glory | elementary | congratulated |

1. When was the last time you _____ someone?

_____

2. For what games is it important to have _____ aim?

_____

3. How is _____ school different from high school?

_____

4. Do any sports teams in your school belong to a _____?

_____

5. Should people play sports for fun or for _____? Explain.

_____

6. Who enjoys sports more—the players or the _____?

_____

Spike This!

Our volleyball team belongs to a city-wide *division*. Most of the teams we play are from other *elementary* schools. Last season, however, we played a middle school team.

We played in their gym, which was very big, so thousands of *onlookers* cheered for the home team. Before the game, our team huddled together to plan our strategy. We knew that if we wanted to play well, we would have to make *accurate* shots. We were not thinking of *glory* then. We just wanted to play our best. It was a great surprise that we won. The next day in school everyone *congratulated* us.

1. What do *onlookers* do at a game? _____

2. What is a word that means "free from mistakes, exactly right"? _____

3. What does it mean to be *congratulated* in this story? _____

_____

4. What *division* did this volleyball team play in? _____

5. Why didn't the team from the *elementary* school expect *glory*? _____

_____

_____

_____

McGraw-Hill School Division

5 Book 5/Unit 3
The Marble Champ

At Home: Have students use the vocabulary words to write about their favorite sport.

76a

Story Comprehension

Think about what happens in the "The Marble Champ." Then complete the story map below.

Setting	1. _____ _____
Traits of Main Character	2. _____ _____
Other Characters	3. _____ _____ _____
Problem	4. _____ _____ _____
Events Leading to Climax	5. _____ _____ _____ _____ _____ _____
Ending	6. _____ _____ _____

At Home: Have students write down what they think the main idea or "major message" is for "The Marble Champ."

McGraw-Hill School Division

Use Pictures and Instructions

When you learn to make or do something by following the steps in a process, you are **following instructions,** or directions.

Read the instructions on how to tie a cat's-paw knot. Then answer each question.

Instructions

The cat's-paw knot is used to attach a rope to a hook. Use a rope about the length of your arm.

1. First hold one part of the rope in each hand.

2. Then twist the two parts in opposite directions, forming two side-by-side eyes, or holes.

3. Now pass the base of the hook through the two eyes of the knot so that a sling hangs from the hook.

It's called a cat's-paw knot because, like a cat, it never loses its grip.

1. What is the main use of a cat's-paw knot? _____

2. How many ropes do you need to tie this knot? _____

3. In what direction do you twist the two parts of the rope? _____

4. What is formed by twisting the two loops? How will the rope look now? _____

_____

5. What is passed through the eyes of the cat's-paw knot? _____

5

Book 5/Unit 3
The Marble Champ

At Home: Have students follow directions to complete a task.

78

Steps in a Process

A series of steps you follow in order are **steps in a process.** Think of the steps in a process you might have used to solve a problem.

Now consider the steps in a process that Lupe followed to make herself the marble champ. Write them down in order. The first step is done for you. You may wish to look back at the story.

1. Lupe decides she wants to win at a sport, and she decides that she might be able to win playing marbles.

2. _____

_____

3. _____

_____

4. _____

_____

5. _____

_____

6. _____

_____

7. _____

_____

8. _____

_____

At Home: Ask students to choose a goal, and then have them write the steps in a process to meet their goal.

Book 5/Unit 3
The Marble Champ 7

McGraw-Hill School Division

Summarize

When you **summarize** a story, you briefly retell it in your own words. In the retelling, you focus on the main characters and the most important events.

Read the story below, and then summarize it.

The city council wanted a mural to go with the new swimming pool. Once the mural contest was announced, all the artists in the city wanted to win. Mela and Troy, two of the best artists in town, hoped to win. Knowing the competition would be tough, Mela and Troy spent two weeks painting and brainstorming in their studio.

Often they painted day and night, not stopping to eat or to sleep. They painted all of their ideas. When it was time to submit their design idea to the city council, they could not decide which one to send. Troy, who was very practical, suggested sending the one that combined most of their ideas.

Waiting for the decision, Mela and Troy panicked. What if their idea was too strange? But the city council chose their design. And so Mela and Troy painted the mural.

Their mural was a giant underwater scene. They wanted people to look at it and feel cool and refreshed and to laugh at it. When the mural was finished, Mela and Troy worried that no one would like it.

The mural was not a typical underwater scene. All sorts of creatures floated and swam in their scene: elephants and dolphins, monkeys in bright red jackets, a giant jellyfish, a giraffe with its neck breaking the surface high above the water—there was even someone in a tuxedo diving to the bottom of the pool to pick up a watch. Mela and Troy weren't sure what people's reaction to their mural would be. They crossed their fingers.

At the unveiling, there was silence. Then children started laughing, and people applauded. Everyone loved the mural. Mela and Troy were happy, too.

Summary _____

_____

_____

_____

_____

Multiple-Meaning Words

Words with more than one meaning are **multiple–meaning words**. Sometimes you need to figure out which meaning is being used. You can use context clues or other words in the sentence or passage to help you figure out the best meaning.

Read each sentence below. Then circle the letter next to the correct meaning of each underlined word.

1. Our school soccer team ranked number one in the league <u>division.</u>

   a. process of dividing numbers   **b.** part of the bigger group

2. The team missed the final <u>match</u> because of rain.

   a. contest   **b.** something identical with another

3. Mara lives five <u>blocks</u> from school.

   a. pieces of hard wood with flat sides   **b.** distances between city streets

4. Ricky chose a bright blue <u>marble</u> for the first target.

   a. highly polished stone used in statues   **b.** a small, glass ball

5. Have you ever seen <u>slate</u> clouds?

   a. bluish-gray   **b.** a flat, smooth, dark bluish-gray rock

6. The rain suddenly started, and we made a <u>dash</u> for cover.

   a. a sudden, fast move   **b.** to stir or throw with violent force

7. We want to <u>beat</u> the team from the other school.

   a. to stir or mix rapidly   **b.** to win against

8. Every Thursday night, the club met for a quilting <u>bee</u>.

   a. a gathering for work or a competition   **b.** a four-winged insect with a stinger

9. Does she have to <u>stamp</u> her feet like that? It is so childish!

   a. to put on a postage stamp   **b.** to put your foot down heavily or loudly

10. At last, they scored the winning <u>point</u>.

   a. a unit used in scoring in a game   **b.** a sharp end

81

At Home: Have students identify and use multiple-meaning words in sentences.

Book 5/Unit 3
The Marble Champ   **10**

Sequence of Events

In a story, events are organized by sequence, or order in which the events occur. Recognizing the **sequence of events** can help you better understand what happens in a story.

Read the story. The story chart below lists the events out of sequence. Number each event in the order in which it happens in the story.

> Ryoko and Tori decided to make popcorn for their friends who had come to watch their new tape. Following their parents' directions, they used one-half cup of corn and two tablespoons of oil. It didn't look like there would be enough popcorn for 12 hungry boys and girls. Ryoko and Tori didn't know what to do.
>
> "I think we need to add more corn," said Ryoko. "What do you think?"
>
> "That makes sense. After all, there are four times as many people eating the popcorn than when Mom and Dad make it. Maybe we should add four times as much," said Tori. Ryoko agreed, so they added four times the amount of corn and oil. They waited until they heard the corn start to pop, and then they joined their friends.
>
> Soon the sound of the corn popping drowned out the movie. It sounded like the fireworks on the Fourth of July. Everyone ran into the kitchen. The popcorn was pushing the lid off the pot. Popcorn was bouncing all over the kitchen. The family dog, Romper, began jumping up to catch the popcorn. Trying to catch the popcorn in paper cups, everyone started laughing. There was popcorn everywhere! No one could catch the popcorn fast enough.
>
> And then Ryoko and Tori's parents walked in.

Story Chart

	The popping corn pushed the lid right off the pot.
	Ryoko and Tori decided to make popcorn for their friends.
	The dog, Romper, started jumping up to catch some popcorn.
	Ryoko and Tori's parents walked into the kitchen.
	Tori says that they should "add four times as much" popcorn.
	The popping corn sounded like Fourth of July fireworks.

At Home: Have students identify the sequence of events for a movie or a book.

McGraw-Hill School Division

Vocabulary

Choose the correct word to complete each sentence.

billowed	heroic	quench	devour	scorched	uprooted

1. The old oak tree was _____ by the tornado.

2. The heat from the raging fire _____ the forest.

3. The volunteers were _____ as they saved seals, otters, and

   sea birds from the oil slick.

4. As the winds blew across the prairie, fields of wheat _____.

5. Ice-cold water can _____ a thirst on a hot day.

6. Must you _____ all the pancakes?

McGraw-Hill School Division

Relief!

For weeks and weeks there was no rain at all. The land was so dry that the plants looked *scorched* from the sun. Irrigating the fields, we made *heroic* efforts to save our crops, but there was not enough water. The blazing sun quickly dried up our meager water supply.

One morning at breakfast, the kitchen curtains suddenly *billowed*. We rushed outside and looked up. Huge rain clouds were racing across the sky. They looked as if they were ready to *devour* the sun. The sky grew dark and stormy. The wind was so strong that it *uprooted* our rose bushes and several plants.

Suddenly the wind stopped and the clouds broke. At long last, rain fell to *quench* the thirsty earth. The rain was a beautiful sight.

1. What does a *scorched* plant look like? _____

_____

2. What sort of efforts were made to save their crops? _____

3. What does a curtain *billowed* with wind look like? _____

4. What verb in this story means "to eat up in a greedy way"? _____

5. What *uprooted* the rose bushes? _____

6. Why was the rain a beautiful sight? _____

_____

_____

6 Book 5/Unit 3
The Paper Dragon

At Home: Have students make a collage using pictures or symbols to represent the vocabulary words.

83a

Story Comprehension

Answer the questions about "The Paper Dragon." You may want to look back at the story.

1. What does Mi Fei love to paint? _____

   _____

2. Why do people come from far away to buy Mi Fei's scrolls? _____

   _____

3. How would you describe Mi Fei's feelings toward his neighbors? ____

   _____

4. Who or what is Sui Jen? Where is Sui Jen from? _____

   _____

5. What is Sui Jen doing to the villages? _____

   _____

6. What has Sui Jen been doing for the past 100 years? _____

7. What do Mi Fei's villagers ask him to do? _____

   _____

   _____

8. Where does Mi Fei find Sui Jen? _____

9. What does Mi Fei reply when Sui Jen asks him to name the most important thing

   that his people created? Why do you think he gives that response? _____

   _____

   _____

10. How does Mi Fei make it possible for the dragon to sleep again? _____

    _____

    _____

At Home: Have students paint a scroll like Mi Fei's. They can use pictures to tell a story.

Book 5/Unit 3
The Paper Dragon 10

McGraw-Hill School Division

Use a Graph

Graphs are a way to "see" and compare data. A **line graph** shows how data changes over time.

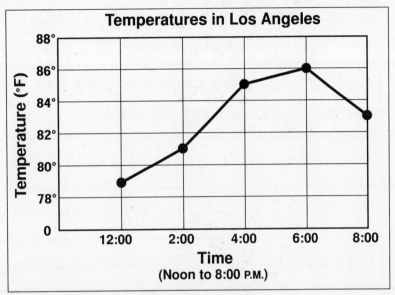

Temperatures in Los Angeles

The line graph shows how temperatures changed between noon and 8:00 P.M. one day in Los Angeles. Use the graph to answer the questions.

1. What is the graph about?

_____

2. When was the temperature the highest? _____

3. Between which two times did the temperature increase the most? How much did it increase? _____

4. Between which two times did the temperature decrease? How much did it decrease? _____

_____

5. Make a prediction. Will the temperature increase or decrease between 8:00 P.M. and 10:00 P.M.? Explain.

_____

_____

At Home: Have students find a temperature graph in the local newspaper. Ask them to discuss how the temperature changed that day.

Sequence of Events

Events in a story happen in a certain **sequence**. Below is a story chart listing events from "The Paper Dragon." Number each event in the order in which it happened. You may refer back to the story for help.

Story Chart

	The dragon Sui Jen becomes smaller and smaller, until it disappears, leaving behind a paper dragon in its place.
	The messenger Mu Wang brings news about the dragon.
	Mi Fei first sees the terrifying sight of the dragon, Sui Jen.
	Mi Fei brings the dragon a paper lantern with a burning candle.
	The villagers plead for Mi Fei's help to stop the dragon.
	Mi Fei begs the dragon to return to one-hundred year's sleep.
	Mi Fei brings the dragon a paper fan.
	Mi Fei climbs up Lung Mountain to find the dragon, Sui Jen.
	Mi Fei brings the dragon a painted scroll showing the faces of all the people he loves.
	Mi Fei is nearly knocked off his feet by the wind from the dragon's tail.

At Home: Ask students to create a story chart of events in their own life.

Summarize

When you **summarize** a story, you briefly retell it in your own words. You explain when and where the story takes place, who the main characters are, and the most important story events.

Read the story below and then summarize it.

Sarko lived on an island in the middle of a lake as big as a sea. Every morning he would paddle out in his canoe to check the fishing lines that he and his parents had set the night before. Many mornings he was joined by his friend, Ta'Ni. Her family and his often fished together.

One morning while Sarko and Ta'Ni were checking the fishing lines, a huge storm suddenly blew in. The lake began to pitch with waves. On the other end of the lake, they could see lightning bolts crack the sky.

"Quick," yelled out Ta'Ni as she paddled alongside Sarko. "Let's paddle together in your canoe so we can get to shore quickly."

Sarko steadied his canoe so that Ta'Ni could safely jump from her canoe to his. Then they both started racing. The rain was falling so heavily that they could barely see the shoreline ahead of them. The waves got bigger and bigger. Eventually, one of the waves flipped the canoe over. Sarko and Ta'Ni found themselves struggling to swim in the cold rough water. They couldn't see over the waves. The thunder roared. They felt as though they were doomed, when suddenly a giant turtle came to their rescue.

Summary _____

_____

_____

_____

_____

_____

McGraw-Hill School Division

5 Book 5/Unit 3
The Paper Dragon

At Home: Ask students to write a summary of their favorite story.

87

Figurative Language: Metaphor

Figurative language creates colorful pictures from words. Writers use figurative language to help readers understand the meaning of something or to help readers see something in a new way. Context clues often help you understand figurative language.

A **metaphor** is one type of figurative language. A metaphor makes an implied comparison. It compares two things you wouldn't usually put together. For example:

In the breeze, the leaves on the trees underline a cheery hello. In this sentence, the metaphor compares tree leaves to hands waving hello.

"The Paper Dragon" has many examples of figurative language. Answer the questions below about the underlined words used in the story.

1. When Mi Fei first hears the <u>roar</u> of the dragon, he thinks his head will <u>burst</u>. What is the dragon's roar being compared to? Will Mi Fei's head really burst?

   _____

   _____

2. The dragon Sui Jen gives nearly impossible tasks to Mi Fei. Some of them sound like metaphors. What does Mi Fei make out of <u>fire wrapped in paper</u>?

   _____

3. At one point, the dragon Sui Jen whips <u>its heavy tail</u> so violently that clouds are <u>swept away</u>. What is its tail being compared to?

   _____

4. While Mi Fei is trying to solve the last task, words begin to *crowd his head*. What are the words being compared to?

   _____

   _____

5. At the end of the story, Mi Fei writes a poem. The first line is "Love can move mountains." Explain how this is a metaphor. What is it being compared to?

   _____

   _____

   _____

At Home: Ask students to write three metaphors.

Steps in a Process

A series of steps that you follow in order are called **steps in a process**.

Each of the following activities has several steps that need to be followed in order. Write numbers 1 through 4 on the lines to show the right order.

Write a Newspaper Article

_____ Interview firefighters and witnesses.

_____ Get a news tip from the fire department.

_____ Return to the newsroom and write your story.

_____ Go to the scene of the fire.

Clean Your Room

_____ Vacuum or sweep the floor.

_____ Dust the surface areas, such as your desk or bureau top.

_____ Pick up all the stuff lying on the floor and on other surfaces.

_____ Sort through the stuff. Put away important things and throw away the rest.

Make an Egg Sandwich

_____ Cook for one minute and place it on toast and serve.

_____ Beat the egg with a fork until it's all the same color.

_____ Crack an egg in a bowl and throw away the shell.

_____ Pour the beaten egg in a frying pan.

Plant a Flower Garden

_____ Find the necessary tools for planting.

_____ Buy flower seeds at the hardware store.

_____ Water and care for the seeds.

_____ Clear out a sunny area and plant the seeds.

At Home: Have students write steps in a process out of sequence. Then have someone in the family put the steps in the correct order.

Vocabulary

In each sentence replace the underlined words with a vocabulary word.

bashful	cemetery	orphanage	canvas	granite	tornado

1. You could see the <u>twister</u> spinning its way across the fields. _____

2. Even though I was hungry, I felt too <u>shy and uncomfortable</u> to ask for something

   to eat. _____

3. On the polished surface of the <u>rock used for building</u>, we could see grains of

   different colors: black, orange, and gray. _____

4. After the war, many children had to go live in <u>a special home for children who had</u>

   <u>lost their parents</u>. _____

5. Traditionally, a <u>graveyard</u> was located at the edge of town. _____

6. The artist used colorful oil paints on a <u>heavy, coarse cotton cloth</u>. _____

90

At Home: Have the students use each vocabulary word in a new sentence.

Book 5/Unit 3
Grandma Essie's Covered Wagon
6

McGraw-Hill School Division

A New Home

Many years ago there was a large, wooden house on the edge of town, just past the *cemetery*. Children with many different backgrounds lived there. For many of the children, the *orphanage* was the only home they had ever known. Some children were curious to know what had happened to their families, but they were too *bashful* to ask.

One spring day a *tornado* came whirling across the plains. Luckily, the children saw it in time to find shelter. After the storm had passed, they came out of the cellar to see their home destroyed.

The townspeople held a huge fair to raise money for a new orphanage. They decided to use *granite* so the building would stand for a long, long time. The children painted a huge *canvas* to hang outside their new home.

1. What is a *cemetery* ? _____

2. What is another word for "timid and uncomfortable"? _____

3. What do you call a place that takes in and cares for children without families?

   _____

4. What else can *canvas* be used for? _____

   _____

5. Why did the children paint a canvas? _____

   _____

   _____

   _____

McGraw-Hill School Division

5

Book 5/Unit 3
Grandma Essie's Covered Wagon

At Home: Have students list things that are made of granite or are granite-colored.

90a

Story Comprehension

Answer the questions about "Grandma Essie's Covered Wagon."

1. At the beginning of the story, where are Essie and her family headed? _____

2. What were the roads like that they traveled on? _____

   _____

3. What was their farmhouse in Kansas like? _____

   _____

4. Why do you think Essie was too bashful to taste the cantaloupe and watermelons

   when she was at the rich boy's house? _____

   _____

5. How did Essie and her brothers and sisters get to school? What did they wear on

   their feet in the summer and fall? _____

   _____

6. Why did they have to sell their Kansas farm? _____

   _____

7. Why did the family leave Kansas for Oklahoma? _____

   _____

8. Why did the father finally buy Stella a pair of white dress shoes? _____

   _____

   _____

At Home: Ask students to illustrate their favorite event from
"Grandma Essie's Covered Wagon."

Book 5/Unit 3
Grandma Essie's Covered Wagon
8

Use a Time Line

A **time line** is a way to organize information in a diagram. Time lines help you keep track of events in the order in which they took place.

Major Events of the Early Twentieth Century

1903 Wright Brothers make the first successful airplane flight (U.S.A.)

1908 Henry Ford produces first Model T car (U.S.A.)

1912 The African National Congress is founded in the Union of South Africa

1914 World War I begins in Europe

1919 World War I ends

1920 Women gain voting rights in the United States

1920 Mahatma Gandhi begins nonviolent protest against British rule in India

1926 John Logie Baird invents the television (England)

Use the time line to answer the questions.

1. What is this time line about? _____

2. How many years does the time line cover? _____

3. What happened in 1919? _____

4. In what year was the African National Congress founded? _____

5. Which happened first: the Wright Brothers' airplane flight or the production of the first Model T car? _____

6. Who began the nonviolent protest against British rule in India? _____

7. Could you have watched the news about women gaining voting rights on television? Explain. _____

_____

8. Tell where this event would go on the time line: In 1910, Japan invaded Korea.

_____

_____

McGraw-Hill School Division

8 Book 5/Unit 3
Grandma Essie's Covered Wagon

At Home: Have students write five important events from their lives on slips of paper, then arrange them in a time line in the order in which they occurred.

92

Steps in a Process

A series of steps you follow in order are called **steps in a process.**

Consider the steps in a process that Papa and Mama took to prepare a wagon for moving the family to Kansas. Write them in order. The first and last steps have already been done for you. You may look back at the story for help.

1. Papa bought a frame wagon.

2. _____
   _____

3. _____
   _____

4. _____
   _____

5. _____
   _____

6. _____
   _____

7. _____
   _____

8. They tied the milk cow and her calf Molly to the back of the wagon.

At Home: Ask students to think about how they might prepare for a trip. Have them write down the steps in a process that they could follow to get ready.

Book 5/Unit 3
Grandma Essie's Covered Wagon
6

Sequence of Events

The **sequence of events** is the order in which things happen in a story. Recognizing the sequence of events can help you better understand a story.

The story events in the chart below are out of sequence. Put these events in order. Number each one so that you have a sensible sequence of events for a story.

Story Chart	Event
	After washing the dishes, we brought buckets of water from the river to put out the campfire. Then we put on our hiking boots.
	At the campsite, we woke up early in the morning, before the sun rose.
	After a cold morning bath, we dressed for a day of work.
	As soon as we finished breakfast, we cleaned the dirty dishes.
	The first thing we did in the morning was to dive into the cold river water.
	I made a huge batch of pancakes and eggs for breakfast.
	Once we were dressed, we gathered firewood for making breakfast.
	Right before we left on our hike, we tied our food into a bundle and hung it on a strong branch high in the trees out of the reach of bears and raccoons.

McGraw-Hill School Division

At Home: Have students write down the sequence of events that occur from the time they leave school in the afternoon until the time they return to school the next morning.

Figurative Language

Figurative language creates colorful word pictures. Recall that a metaphor is one type of figurative language. A **metaphor** makes an implied comparison, or one that is not compared directly. It compares two things you wouldn't usually put together. A **simile** also compares two unlike things, but it makes an explicit comparison, that is, it compares them directly. A simile uses the words **like** or **as**. For example: The boy bolted from the yard <u>like a wild horse.</u> This simile compares a boy to a wild horse.

"Grandma Essie's Covered Wagon" has many examples of figurative language. Answer these questions about metaphors and similes used in the story.

1. When Grandma Essie <u>refers</u> to the covered wagon as a <u>magic ship,</u> is she using a metaphor or a simile? How can you tell. _____

    _____

2. When Grandma Essie describes the prairie rolling on forever <u>like the back of some</u> <u>huge animal</u>, is she using a metaphor or simile? How can you tell? _____

    _____

3. Recalling the time Grandma Essie saw a tornado, she says, "The air was as thick as a stampede." What does she mean by this figurative language? _____

    _____

    _____

4. Is the example above a simile or a metaphor? _____

5. When Grandma Essie describes Opal's newborn baby <u>"as big as a hand"</u>, is she using a metaphor or simile? How can you tell? _____

    _____

6. Is Grandma Essie using a metaphor when she recalls leaving Kansas and "the sight of our own farm floating away"? What does she mean? _____

    _____

    _____

At Home: Ask students to write five examples of figurative language. Encourage them to use both similes and metaphors.

95

Book 5/Unit 3   6
Grandma Essie's Covered Wagon

McGraw-Hill School Division

Author's Purpose and Point of View

All authors have a purpose, or a reason, for writing. The **author's purpose** can be to inform, to entertain, or to persuade the reader. The **point of view** is the perspective from which a story is told. First-person pronouns —*I, me, we, us* —tell you that the first–person point of view is being used. Third-person pronouns—*he, she, they*—tell you that the third-person point of view is being used.

In nonfiction writing, the author often uses the first-person point of view when the purpose is to persuade or to entertain. The author is likely to use the third-person point of view when the purpose is to inform.

Read each passage and complete the chart below. Then answer the two questions.

A. I strongly encourage you to give me your old bicycle. You hardly ever use it anymore. That bicycle just sits in the garage all day gathering dust. Let me take it off your hands and put it to good use.

B. Bluebirds are small colorful birds that live throughout North America. There are three main types of bluebirds: the eastern bluebird, the western bluebird, and the mountain bluebird. Bluebirds usually fly south for the winter and return early in spring.

Passage	Purpose	Point of View
A	1.	2.
B	3.	4.

5. What would be the author's purpose for writing a social studies textbook? _____

_____

6. What point of view would you find in a social studies textbook? Explain. _____

_____

_____

At Home: Ask students to identify the point of view and author's purpose in various stories. Encourage them to use this chart as a model.

Vocabulary

Answer the questions using the vocabulary words.

1. **heritage**   What would you consider to be the most important part of our nation's

heritage? _____

_____

2. **influenced**   Who has greatly influenced United States history? _____

_____

_____

3. **livestock**   Where would you most likely find livestock? _____

_____

4. **survival**   Why might stories about people's survival be important to read? _____

_____

_____

5. **thrive**   What would people have to do to make a town thrive? _____

_____

6. **tiresome**   What things can be tiresome? _____

_____

At Home: Have students use each of the vocabulary words
in a sentence.

Book 5/Unit 3   6
Going Back Home

McGraw-Hill School Division

Windmills in the West

Did you know that windmills were an important part of ranchers settling the West? One of the things that the West needed most was water—it was very important for *survival*. Windmills were used to pump water from deep beneath the ground. This is how ranchers were able to water their *livestock* and fields. Eventually, windmills helped ranches to *thrive*.

Few other things have *influenced* the West as much as the windmill, except perhaps for the railroad. Of course, it is not *tiresome* to hear about all of that now—because many people like history and knowing about our nation's *heritage*.

1. What does *tiresome* mean? _____

2. What is a word that means "to be successful"? _____

3. What is an example of *livestock?* _____

   _____

4. What do you call something that is passed down from earlier generations? _____

5. How was it that windmills *influenced* survival in the West? _____

   _____

   _____

McGraw-Hill School Division

At Home: Have students write about their concept of heritage. Ask them, "What do you think is important to pass down from one generation to the next?" Explain why.

Story Comprehension

Think about the ideas expressed in "Going Back Home." Then answer these questions. You may look back at the story for help.

1. How does the artist in "Going Back Home" learn about her family? _____

_____

_____

2. Why does the artist in "Going Back Home" create quilt-like backgrounds in her art?

_____

_____

3. How does an artist like the one in "Going Back Home" use pictures? _____

_____

_____

4. What does the black pot in the picture "Inheritors of Slavery" symbolize? _____

_____

_____

5. Why does the artist make the well the central image in one of her paintings? Why is

there a wheel on the well? _____

_____

6. What are the "blues"? Where did they originally come from? _____

_____

_____

_____

At Home: Have students draw a scene from "Going Back Home."

Read a Family Tree

A **family tree** is a diagram that can help you track the people from your family's past. In this family tree, the circles stand for the females and the boxes stand for the males. The lines connecting boxes across marked with an "M" indicate a marriage. Lines going down indicate offspring, or children from a marriage.

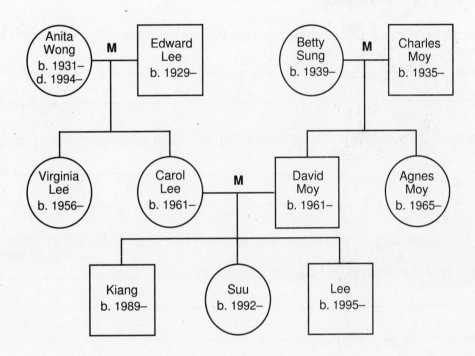

1. How many generations does this family tree show? _____

2. How are Carol Lee and David Moy related? _____

3. How are Kiang and Suu related? _____

4. Is Lee a boy or a girl and how do you know? _____

   _____

5. How are Virginia Lee and Agnes Moy related? _____

   _____

6. According to the family tree, who is no longer living? _____

   _____

Author's Purpose and Point of View

All **authors** have a **purpose** for writing. The author's purpose can be to inform, to entertain, or to persuade the reader. Many authors of nonfiction write to inform the reader. Nonfiction writers often use the first-person **point of view** when they are expressing a personal opinion or relating a personal experience.

1. What do you think the author's purpose was for writing "Going Back Home"? Explain

   why. _____

   _____

2. Whose is the point of view in "Going Back Home"? How do you know? _____

   _____

   _____

3. When the artist/narrator writes about the meaning of the symbols in her paintings, is

   her main purpose to inform, to entertain, or to persuade? Explain. _____

   _____

   _____

   _____

4. When the artist/narrator writes about her self-portrait, is her main purpose to inform,

   to entertain, or to persuade? Explain. _____

   _____

   _____

5. In what ways might the narrator's purpose for writing "Going Back Home" be to

   persuade people? _____

   _____

   _____

   _____

At Home: Ask students to find something written in the
third-person for the purpose to entertain.

McGraw-Hill School Division

Summarize

When you **summarize** nonfiction, you briefly explain—in your own words—the subject or topic of the article and the article's most important ideas.

Read the nonfiction piece below, and then summarize it.

Scientists are looking for ways to make quiet airplanes. They are studying the owl for design ideas. Owls are one of the quietest birds in flight. They are so quiet that their prey— rabbits and field mice that they hunt from the sky—never hear them coming.

What makes airplanes so noisy? When you hear a plane overhead, it's not only the engine's roar making all that noise. There is also the sound of wind rushing over the aircraft, and the sound of the plane's wings slicing through the air.

Scientists have already worked to lower engine noise in airplanes. Now they are trying to reduce the noise made by the movement of a plane's wings. Scientists are studying how owls are able to fly without creating any noise in the air. To do this, they focus on how air flows across the owl's wings.

Someday scientists hope to figure out how to change the wing design of an airplane so that it makes less noise in flight. The idea might come from the owl!

Summary _____

_____

_____

_____

_____

_____

Multiple-Meaning Words

Words with more than one meaning are **multiple-meaning words**. Sometimes you need to figure out which meaning is being used. You can use context clues, or other words in the sentence or passage, to help you figure out the meaning.

Read each sentence below. Then circle the letter next to the correct meaning of each underlined word.

1. She was a strong woman of much <u>might</u>.

   a. helping verb that shows doubt   **b.** power, force

2. I <u>might</u> have visited Mount Vernon once.

   a. helping verb that shows doubt   **b.** power, force

3. She <u>drew</u> her self–portrait in charcoal.

   a. sketched   **b.** pulled

4. Every night at six o'clock, he <u>drew</u> the curtains closed.

   a. sketched   **b.** pulled

5. We did not do <u>well</u> in the second game.

   a. in a good or satisfactory way; better   **b.** deep hole in the ground

6. They used a bucket to draw water from the <u>well</u>.

   a. in a good or satisfactory way; better   **b.** deep hole in the ground

7. He was depressed and suffered from the <u>blues</u> last week.

   a. low spirits; depression   **b.** musical style of songs

8. He wrote a book about the history of the <u>blues</u> in the Mississippi Delta.

   a. low spirits; depression   **b.** musical style of songs

9. On hot summer nights, we sat out on the front <u>stoop</u> and told stories.

   a. small staircase or front porch   **b.** to lower oneself

10. Can you <u>stoop</u> down and get that for me?

    a. small staircase or front porch   **b.** to lower oneself

At Home: Ask students to list multiple-meaning words and record any new definitions they learn.

Book 5/Unit 3
Going Back Home 10

McGraw-Hill School Division

Sequence of Events

Events in a story happen in a certain sequence, or order. Recognizing the **sequence of events** helps you make better sense of a story.

Read the story. The chart below the story lists the story events that are out of order. Number each event in the correct order.

It was time for Jaqui to clean out Gi-Gi's glass home. Gi-Gi was her hamster. First she had to make sure that all cats were out of her room. Then she locked her door so they couldn't get in. The cats and Gi-Gi were not best friends.

Finding the old shoebox with holes poked in it, Jaqui placed Gi-Gi in it and closed the lid. She watched the box for a short time to make sure Gi-Gi was safe and wouldn't try to get out.

First Jaqui emptied all the old cedar chips from the glass cage into a plastic bag and threw them out. Then she lined the bottom of the cage with a newspaper and put in a big pile of fresh cedar chips over the newspaper. Next she filled the water tube and put fresh food in Gi-Gi's dish. Jaqui also added the cardboard roll from the paper towel for Gi-Gi to chew. Finally, she put Gi-Gi back into her glass house. Gi-Gi seemed to smile at Jaqui as she explored the clean house.

Sequence	Event
	She locks the door to keep the cats out.
	Jaqui puts fresh cedar chips into Gi-Gi's glass cage.
	Jaqui finds the old shoebox and puts Gi-Gi in it.
	Jaqui throws away the old cedar chips and lines the cage with newspaper.
	She fills the water tube and feeding dish.
	She puts Gi-Gi into her glass cage.
	Jaqui makes sure no cats are in the room.
	Jaqui watches Gi-Gi to make sure that she is fine in the shoebox.

8 Book 5/Unit 3
A Mountain of a Monument

At Home: Have students identify the sequence of events for a chore they do at home.

103

Vocabulary

Replace the underlined words in each sentence with a vocabulary word.

awesome	explosives	nostril	dedicate	hail	sculpture

1. The construction workers use <u>something that causes an explosion</u> to clear huge

   rocks from the land. _____

2. We want to <u>devote a special part of</u> the community garden in honor of the woman

   who started it. _____

3. If I could, I would make a <u>carving in stone</u> of a waterfall. _____

4. We could hear the crowd <u>congratulate and cheer</u> the winning team.

   _____

5. Watching the whales leaping in the water was a truly <u>wondrous</u> sight.

   _____

6. I had to put my hay fever medicine in each <u>opening of my nose</u>

   so I could breathe. _____

104

At Home: Have students use each of the vocabulary words
in a sentence.

Book 5/Unit 3
A Mountain of a Monument
6

Hail to the New Year!

Each year on New Year's Eve, the community leaders *dedicate* the center of the city park for a giant ice-carving contest. This year I went with my friends to watch. It was awesome to see the artists quickly carve so many details. My favorite *sculpture* was the giant swan.

At midnight, everyone in the great crowd cheered as colorful *explosives* called fireworks went off to bring in the New Year. I enjoyed seeing the brilliant colors, but I wished I could put a plug in each *nostril* so that I didn't have to smell the smoke.

1. What do you call a kind of statue that is carved out of ice? _____

   _____

2. What does the word *dedicate* mean as it is used here? _____

   _____

3. What does the word *hail* mean as it is used in the title? _____

4. What word in this story means "extraordinary" or "wonderful"? _____

5. How do you think the author felt about the New Year's celebration? _____

   _____

   _____

   _____

McGraw-Hill School Division

At Home: Have students describe something that they think is *awesome*.

Story Comprehension

Answer the questions about "A Mountain of a Monument." You may look back at the story for help.

1. The mountain of a monument is a memorial to whom? Where is it? _____
   _____

2. Who was Chief Crazy Horse? _____
   _____

3. What did Crazy Horse do that made him famous? _____
   _____

4. How old was Crazy Horse when he died? _____

5. How long have people been working on the statue? _____

6. Who first came up with the idea of designing a huge statue, and when? _____
   _____

7. Who was the artist who actually designed the statue? _____

8. How will the statue be unique when it is finished? _____
   _____

9. What do workers have to do twice a year to help carve the statue out of mountain
   rock? _____

10. When may the statue be finished, and what will it look like? _____
    _____
    _____

At Home: Have students write about a monument or memorial that they have seen and tell why it is special.

Book 5/Unit 3
A Mountain of a Monument
10

McGraw-Hill School Division

Use Scale Drawings

Use this architect's drawing to answer the following questions.

1. What does this blueprint show you? _____

2. Who would need to use this blueprint? _____

_____

3. Where are most of the windows on this house? _____

_____

4. Is this a two-story house? How can you tell? _____

_____

5. How many bedrooms are in this house? _____

_____

6. How many closets are in the house? _____

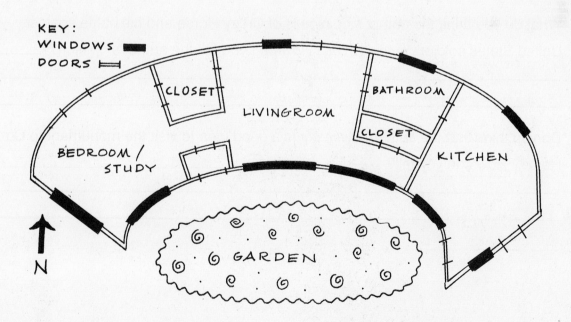

6 Book 5/Unit 3
A Mountain of a Monument

At Home: Encourage students to design a floor plan in a
blueprint form.

106

Author's Purpose and Point of View

Most authors of nonfiction write mainly to inform. As they present information, authors often reveal their **point of view**, or personal opinion, especially when they are writing to persuade or describe a personal experience. Nonfiction writers may also write to entertain.

Answer these questions about "A Mountain of a Monument."

1. Is the purpose of the author of this article mainly to inform? Explain. _____
_____
_____

2. The author refers to the monument as an awesome sight. Do you think this is an expression of personal opinion? Explain. _____
_____
_____

3. Do you think that the author personally visited the Crazy Horse Memorial? Explain.
_____
_____
_____

4. What do you think the author's opinion is of Crazy Horse and his battle against United States soldiers in the 1870s? How can you tell the author's opinion? _____
_____
_____

5. Do you think that the author believes it is a good idea to visit the monument to Crazy Horse? How can you tell? _____
_____
_____

At Home: Have students write about a monument they would create for their favorite leader.

107

Book 5/Unit 3
A Mountain of a Monument
5

Multiple-Meaning Words

Words with more than one meaning are **multiple-meaning words**. You can use context clues or other words in the sentence or passage to help you figure out how the word used is being used.

Read each sentence below. Then circle the letter next to the correct meaning of each underlined word.

1. As soon as the President walks in the room, the band plays "<u>Hail</u> to the Chief."

   a. congratulate or cheer   **b.** frozen rain

2. What is it that she <u>states</u> in her letter to the governor?

   a. sections of a country   **b.** expresses in words

3. My parents had some <u>reservations</u> about letting me go out.

   a. land set aside for a special purpose   **b.** doubts

4. The new store manager asked me about my <u>background</u> in sales.

   a. a person's past experience, education, or training

   b. part of a scene in a play that appears far away

5. Please put those groceries in the <u>back</u> of the car.

   a. in return   **b.** toward the rear

6. The baseball player, Joe DiMaggio, was a <u>giant</u> in his time.

   a. someone very powerful or important   **b.** an unusually tall person

7. We all have the <u>right</u> to free speech.

   a. the opposite of left   **b.** a claim that is protected by the law

8. One student told the class that medicine was his chosen <u>field</u>.

   a. a piece of open land   **b.** an area of interest

8   Book 5/Unit 3
A Mountain of a Monument

At Home: Ask students to write sentences for other multiple-meaning words from this selection: blast and peak. Each sentence should cover one meaning of the word.

108

McGraw-Hill School Division

Figurative Language

Figurative language creates colorful pictures from words. Writers use figurative language to help readers see something in a new way. Context clues can often help you understand how figurative language is being used in a story.

A **metaphor** is one type of figurative language. A metaphor makes an implied comparison by comparing two things you would not usually put together. For example:

<u>My old friend</u>, <u>the sea</u>, came out to greet me.

In this sentence, the metaphor compares <u>the sea</u> to an <u>old friend</u>.

In the sentences below, explain what two unlike things each metaphor is comparing.

1. Each morning we bit into <u>hockey pucks</u>—the stale muffins that only our camp

   kitchen could bake. ——————————————————————

2. In the <u>springtime</u> of our youth, we could easily dance the night away. _____

   _____

3. The tulips formed a row of <u>colorful, silent bells</u> blowing in the breeze. _____

   _____

4. The basketball team <u>thundered</u> down the court. _____

   _____

5. Each basketball shot became a <u>lightning bolt</u> zapping the other team. _____

   _____

At Home: Ask students to write metaphors about their everyday activities, such as school or sports.

McGraw-Hill School Division

Unit 3 Vocabulary Review

A. Read each word in column 1. Find its antonym, or the word most nearly opposite in meaning, in column 2. Then write the letter of the opposite word on the line next to the word in column 1.

_____ 1. uprooted   **a.** fail

_____ 2. awesome   **b.** shame

_____ 3. glory   **c.** outgoing, confident

_____ 4. bashful   **d.** exciting

_____ 5. thrive   **e.** dull, ordinary

_____ 6. tiresome   **f.** planted

B. Supply the correct vocabulary word.

cemetery	dedicate	devour	heritage	influenced	quench

1. Did you know that there is a special _____ where people bury pets?

2. Two bear cubs can quickly _____ a bushel of blueberries.

3. To whom did the writer _____ his latest mystery novel?

4. The right to free speech is part of our national _____.

5. What ideas or people have _____ your life for the better?

6. Drinking ice-cold lemonade on a hot day is a great way to _____ your thirst.

12   Book 5/Unit 3
Unit 3 Vocabulary Review

At Home: Have students write a sentence for each vocabulary word in Part A.

110

Unit 3 Vocabulary Review

A. Answer each question.

1. **accurate**   Why is it important to use accurate facts when writing a history report for school? _____

_____

2. **heroic**   What does it mean to be a heroic person? Give some examples of heroic people _____

_____

3. **tornado**   What is a tornado? What destruction could a tornado cause?

_____

_____

4. **explosives** Why should you be careful around explosives? _____

_____

5. **sculpture**   What do you need to create a piece of sculpture? What things could you use to make a sculpture? _____

_____

B. Write the vocabulary word that means almost the same thing as the underlined word.

survival	bashful	scorched	tornado	onlookers

1. The forest fire <u>burned</u> the log cabin at the edge of the woods. _____

2. Lance was somewhat <u>shy</u> when you first met him. _____

3. Luckily the <u>twister</u> did little damage to the small town. _____

4. Rain and sunshine are both important for the <u>life</u> of a plant. _____

5. There were a number of <u>bystanders</u> watching the football game. _____

At Home: Have students make up their own sentences using the vocabulary words.

McGraw-Hill School Division

Judgments & Decisions

Before you make a **decision** about something, you consider the reasons for and against the decision. Read each situation below. List two reasons for each choice, and then make a **judgment** about what you should do. Write your final decision.

Suppose the following: After three weekends in a row of cold rain, this weekend is sunny and warm. You are having friends over for two hours. One of them is bringing a new video that you want to see. How would you decide to spend the day? Should you stay indoors, or should you go outside?

1. Two reasons for staying indoors: _____

_____

_____

2. Two reasons for going outdoors: _____

_____

_____

3. Final decision: _____

_____

Suppose the following: Two of your friends have had a misunderstanding that has led to bad feelings between them. Should you try to get them to be friends again, or should you let them figure things out on their own?

1. Two reasons for trying to get them to be friends again: _____

_____

_____

2. Two reasons for letting them figure things out on their own: _____

_____

_____

3. Final decision: _____

_____

_____

McGraw-Hill School Division

6 Book 5/Unit 4 **Carlos and the Skunk**

At Home: Have students list the reasons why they should and should not buy something. Then ask them to make a judgment about what they should do and write their final decision.

112

Vocabulary

Write a vocabulary word from the list that means almost the same thing as the underlined words in the sentences.

nestled	peculiar	stunned	tortillas	unbearable	unpleasant

1. The cold water was _____. The temperature was <u>intolerable</u>.

2. The star of the film was very _____. She had a <u>disagreeable</u> personality.

3. We were all <u>shocked</u> to hear she had won the prize. It _____ us.

4. I like _____. They remind me of thin <u>pancakes</u>.

5. After a long day of hiking, we lay comfortably _____ in our tent. That

   night we <u>snuggled</u> in our sleeping bags to stay warm.

6. The story is a little <u>odd</u>. Some people think what happened is _____.

At Home: Have students use the vocabulary words in sentences

Book 5/Unit 4
Carlos and the Skunk

6

Very Good Cooking

"I could go for some good food," Maria thought to herself. "I could go for some *tortillas*. I could make them myself. How hard could it be?"

Usually, Maria thought cooking was *unpleasant*, but this time she was actually enjoying herself. Maria poured corn flour and water into a bowl just like she had seen her grandmother do. "That's *peculiar*," said Maria. "There must be more ingredients in the recipe." But Maria didn't have the recipe. So she decided to create her own. She found a box of raisins *nestled* in a drawer. She added those. Then she added some molasses and a little sugar.

Maria was finishing cooking her tortillas when her grandmother came into the kitchen. Maria proudly told her the recipe she had invented. Her grandmother was *stunned*. "Well, normally, you need only flour and water, but yours does sound interesting. I'm sure it won't be *unbearable*," said her grandmother. "I'm sure we'll enjoy eating them." They did enjoy eating them. They were very good!

1. What did Maria decide to cook? _____

2. What did Maria think was *peculiar*? _____

_____

3. What was *nestled* in the drawer? _____

4. How did Maria's grandmother react to her recipe? _____

5. Why do you think Maria's grandmother said the tortillas would not be *unbearable*?

_____

_____

5

Book 5/Unit 4
Carlos and the Skunk

At Home: Have students write a story about a time they cooked.

113a

McGraw-Hill School Division

Story Comprehension

Answer the questions about "Carlos and the Skunk."

1. Who is Gloria? Is she a main character? Why is she important to the story? _____

   _____

   _____

2. What happens to Carlos's feelings for Gloria as they grow older? _____

   _____

   _____

3. Who is Dos Dedos (Two Toes)? Why is Dos Dedos important to the story? _____

   _____

   _____

4. What does Carlos think will happen if he picks up the skunk by its tail? _____

   _____

5. How does Carlos try to get rid of the skunk smell? _____

   _____

   _____

6. How does the fact that Carlos forgets to clean his shoes affect the plot? _____

   _____

7. What happens at church that embarrasses Carlos? _____

   _____

8. How do you know Carlos's father knows about the skunk and Carlos's smelly

   shoes? Explain._____

   _____

Read a Diagram

A **diagram** is a simple drawing of an object. In a diagram, the important parts of an object are labeled. Below is the diagram of a suspension bridge.

Use the diagram to answer these questions.

1. What part of the bridge supports the towers from below? _____

2. How is the bridge supported from above? _____

_____

3. What is the name of the part of the bridge where the cables run over the top of the

tower? _____

4. How are the cables anchored to the ground at each end of the bridge? _____

_____

5. Cables are heavy ropes of twisted steel. What do you think would happen if the

ends of the cables were not anchored into the ground? _____

_____

_____

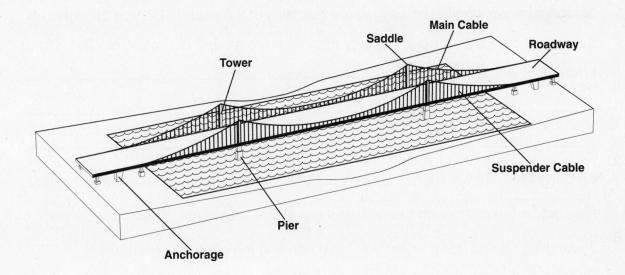

Book 5/Unit 4
Carlos and the Skunk
5

At Home: Have students look up other types of bridges and make a diagram for one of them.

115

McGraw-Hill School Division

Judgments & Decisions

When reading a story, you make **judgments** about the characters and the things they say or do. Think about the **decisions** made by the main characters in "Carlos and the Skunk." Answer each question below. Then explain your answers.

1. "Carlos, you'd better be careful," whispered Gloria as Carlos inched along on his stomach near the skunk. In your opinion, do you think this was wise advice? Why or why not? _____

_____

_____

2. Beginning to think he (Carlos) smelled better, he crawled into bed and fell asleep quickly after his very unpleasant day. Why do you think Carlos went straight to bed? Was what happened to Carlos unpleasant? _____

_____

_____

3. The women began vigorously fanning their faces with their church programs. The children started squirming and pinched their noses. Little by little the strange behavior began working its way toward the back of the church. Do you think this is the way people should act when they are in a large group? Do you think Carlos' dad knew what was going on? _____

_____

_____

4. Embarrassed, Carlos pushed his way out of the church. He heard Gloria calling to him, but he bolted through the door and ran all the way home. Would you do the same thing Carlos did or would you have handled the situation differently?

_____

_____

At Home: Encourage students to talk about one thing that a main character in "Carlos and the Skunk" said or did that, in their opinion, was either right or wrong. Ask them to explain their opinions.

Book 5/Unit 4
Carlos and the Skunk
4

McGraw-Hill School Division

Draw Conclusions

Since authors don't always tell readers exactly how the characters in a story feel, it is necessary to **draw** your own **conclusions**. To draw a conclusion, you rely on what you know from your own life experience and story clues.

Read the situations below and answer each question. Then describe the clues that helped you draw each conclusion. Use one clue from the story, and one from your own life experience.

In the long afternoon sun, Sula and Kwame swung gently back and forth on the porch swing. They were talking quietly, sharing their thoughts with each other, when three of their pals from school came by. They asked Sula and Kwame if they wanted to walk to the store with them. "No, thanks," said Kwame.
"We're sort of busy right now," explained Sula.

1. How do Sula and Kwame feel about each other? _____

_____

2. **Story clue:** _____

3. **Life Experience clue:** _____

_____

Julia stomped down the hallway to her room. Then Arnie and Mrs. Kosasky heard the loud slam of a door. Arnie didn't know what to do or say. After a few awkward seconds that seemed to last forever, he turned to Mrs. Kosasky and said, "Well, I guess I'd better be going now, or I'll be late for the game. Thanks for lunch."

4. How does Julia feel? _____

5. **Story clue:** _____

6. **Life Experience clue:** _____

_____

_____

McGraw-Hill School Division

⑥ Book 5/Unit 4
Carlos and the Skunk

At Home: Ask students to draw conclusions about the characters in their favorite book.

117

Suffixes

A **suffix** is a word part that can be added to the end of a word to change the word's meaning. Knowing what a suffix means can help you define the word. The suffix -*less* means "not having" or "without." The suffix -*able* means "able to be" or "cause to be."

Word	+	Suffix =	New Word	Meaning
hope	+	less =	hopeless	without hope
bear	+	able =	bearable	tolerable

Write the suffix of each word. Write the word's meaning. Then use the word in a sentence of your own.

1. breathless   **Suffix:** _____   **Meaning:** _____

   Sentence: _____

2. likable   **Suffix:** _____   **Meaning:** _____

   Sentence: _____

3. powerful   **Suffix:** _____   **Meaning:** _____

   Sentence: _____

4. laughable   **Suffix:** _____   **Meaning:** _____

   Sentence: _____

5. homeless   **Suffix:** _____   **Meaning:** _____

   Sentence: _____

6. thoughtful   **Suffix:** _____   **Meaning:** _____

   Sentence: _____

7. youthful   **Suffix:** _____   **Meaning:** _____

   Sentence: _____

8. agreeable   **Suffix:** _____   **Meaning:** _____

   Sentence: _____

At Home: Ask students to name two other words that end with -*ful* and two other words that end with -*less*. Have them write each word's meaning, and then use each word in a sentence.

118

Book 5/Unit 4
Carlos and the Skunk

8

McGraw-Hill School Division

Important & Unimportant Information

Nonfiction writing includes **important** information that supports the main idea. There is also **unimportant** information that makes the selection interesting or fun to read, but may not directly support the main idea.

Read the paragraph below. Decide what information is important and what information is unimportant. Write **I** next to the sentence if the information is important, and **U** next to the sentence if the information is unimportant.

Watching too much television can be dangerous for your health. There are good programs on television, but watching too much television is not good for anyone. The average fifth grader in North America watches 25 hours of television a week. That's at least three and a half hours a day spent sitting in front of a television instead of doing something productive. Children could spend more time actively doing things to develop their minds and bodies. Besides watching television, they can do things such as playing baseball or another sport, playing an instrument, walking, dancing, working on a science project, or reading. Being physically active helps keep weight down and muscles strong. Taking part in team sports teaches the important skill of interacting with others.

_____ 1. Watching too much television can be dangerous for your health.

_____ 2. There are good programs on television.

_____ 3. Children need to spend more time actively doing things to develop their minds and their bodies.

_____ 4. Being active in body and mind is healthier than sitting and watching television.

_____ 5. Children can do many things besides watching television, such as playing baseball or another sport, playing an instrument, walking, dancing, working on a science project, or reading.

5 Book 5/Unit 4
How to Think Like a Scientist

At Home: Have students create a list of activities that they can do instead of watching television.

119

Vocabulary

Label each sentence **True** or **False.** If a sentence is false, write the correct definition of the word in italics.

1. If you think carefully before answering a question, you are answering *automatically.*
    _____ _____

2. Things you see and take note of are *observations.* _____
    _____

3. If you get many *assignments* in different subjects you have a lot of homework to do.
    _____ _____

4. Crossing a busy street *carelessly* is not dangerous. _____
    _____

5. If you ride your bike to school every day, then you don't *normally* take the school bus or walk there. _____ _____

6. If you drove carefully and slowly up a winding mountain road, you would have *swerved* often. _____ _____
    _____

At Home: Have students use each of the vocabulary words in a sentence.

Book 5/Unit 4
How to Think Like a Scientist ◻ 6

McGraw-Hill School Division

Stay Alert!

Every Wednesday at two o'clock, Ms. Yee *automatically* hands out homework. She gives us *assignments* for four subjects: math, English, social studies, and earth sciences. *Normally* I am the first student to get any handouts because I sit right next to her desk.

This time, however, Ms. Yee *swerved* around my desk and went directly to the back of the room. When she was finished, she asked us if we had noticed anything different about the way she had handed out the homework today. A few of us remarked that she had begun at the back of the room, which was unusual.

"Good." said Ms. Yee. "I want you all to get into the habit of making *observations* about things. Lately, some of you have been working *carelessly*—you need to pay closer attention to your work."

1. What does it mean to do something *automatically*? _____

_____

2. What is a word that means "tasks or jobs that have been given out"? _____

3. What is another word for "usually"? _____

4. What does it mean to make *observations*? _____

5. Ms. Yee *swerved* around the student's desk at the front and went directly to the

back of the room. Why did she do this? _____

_____

_____

At Home: Have students write about some observations they have made at school.

Story Comprehension

The author of "How to Think Like a Scientist" asks questions for which there are correct answers and then offers reasons for why people give incorrect answers. Use what you learned in "How to Think Like a Scientist" to complete the chart below. Begin by stating the question asked in the beginning of the three sections listed below.

Question	Correct Answer	Reason for Incorrect Answer
Watching the Murphys: 1.	2.	3.
The Zoo Comes to the Classroom: 4.	5.	6.
The Math Assignment: 7.	8.	9.

10. What was the author's purpose for writing "How to Think Like a Scientist"? ——

_____

_____

_____

_____

At Home: Have students retell the story and explain why people sometimes give incorrect answers.

McGraw-Hill School Division

Use an Outline

Using an **outline** can help you to group facts and organize information. In an outline, a Roman numeral is placed before each main idea. Beneath that, capital letters organize the important facts that support the main idea. Study this section of an outline. Then answer the questions below.

III. Women Pilots in the Thirties
  A. Beryl Markham survives crash on Cape Breton.
  B. Jean Batten sets record for South Atlantic Flight.
  C. Louise Thaden wins Bendix Trophy in 1936.
  D. Amelia Earhart makes last flight, 1937.

1. Which section of the outline is presented here? _____

2. What is the main idea of this section? How do you know what it is about?

_____

_____

3. What sort of information follows the capital letters? _____

_____

4. If you found out about another woman pilot in the 1930s, how would you include her in the outline? Explain. _____

_____

_____

5. How could you use an outline to help you study a textbook to prepare for a test?

_____

_____

5 Book 5/Unit 4
How to Think Like a Scientist

At Home: Encourage students to explain how they would use an outline for their next research report.

122

Important & Unimportant Information

In "How to Think Like A Scientist," the **important information** supports the main idea of the article, which is *how to answer questions correctly*.

Place a ✓ next to each sentence that states important information from "How to Think Like A Scientist." You may look back at the story for help.

_____ **1.** You must use information carefully to answer a question correctly.

_____ **2.** Ralphie really did see men taking things out of the Murphy's house.

_____ **3.** The gastromorph is a dangerous fish that will bite you if you put your hand in the fish bowl.

_____ **4.** Don't base your answer on what someone else says.

_____ **5.** One girl knew the fish were really guppies because her sister had some at home.

_____ **6.** You will probably make mistakes if you depend too much on other people's answers to questions.

_____ **7.** Sometimes we choose an answer to a question because it is the answer we like, and that can lead to making the wrong choice.

_____ **8.** If a great movie is playing and you have a math assignment due the next morning, it's best to spend the evening at home working on your math.

_____ **9.** At class on Monday morning, Pat asked Ms. Wilson how her weekend was, hoping that she'd then forget to ask for the math assignments.

_____ **10.** Finding an answer that is correct is more difficult than finding an answer you like.

At Home: Encourage students to talk about the most important information they learned from reading "How to Think Like a Scientist."

Book 5/Unit 4
How to Think Like a Scientist
10

McGraw-Hill School Division

Draw Conclusions

Since authors don't always tell readers exactly how the characters in a story feel, you must sometimes draw your own conclusions. To **draw a conclusion**, you rely on what you know from personal life experience and story clues.

Read the situation below, and answer each question. Then describe the clues that helped you draw each conclusion.

> Andrea and Mario had been working in their grandfather's garden all afternoon. Mario squinted into the sun. It was time for a rest. He slumped down in the shade and wiped his sweaty brow. Then he reached for the water bottle for a cool, refreshing drink. Andrea stopped weeding and joined him under the pear tree. He passed her the cold water bottle from their picnic basket. Andrea quickly gulped down what was left of it. As usual, Mario hadn't left much for her. Andrea went to back to work, while Mario rested.

1. From what you just read, how do you think Andrea and Mario are related? _____

_____

2. Story clue: _____

_____

3. What is the weather like? _____

4. Story clue: _____

_____

5. What kind of worker is Andrea? _____

_____

6. Story clue: _____

_____

McGraw-Hill School Division

6 Book 5/Unit 4
How to Think Like a Scientist

At Home: Encourage students to draw conclusions about some stories that they have read.

124

Root Words

You can make a **root word** into another word by adding a prefix or a suffix. For example, the word *fresh* is the root word for the words re*fresh* and *fresh*ness. Knowing the meaning of the root word can help you define unknown words. For example, the word aquarium has a root word aqua that means water. Often root words originally come from the ancient Latin and Greek languages.

Root Word	Meaning	Language of Origin
aqua	water	Latin
tele	far off	Greek
phone	voice, sound	Greek
form	shape, form	Latin

Use the root word chart above to write the root of each word below.

1. aquatic _____

2. telescope _____

3. phonics _____

4. information _____

5. headphone _____

6. aquamarine _____

7. telephone _____

8. aquaplane _____

9. formula _____

10. microphone _____

11. aqueduct _____

12. misinform _____

Choose four words from above, and write a sentence using each word.

13. _____

14. _____

15. _____

16. _____

At Home: Have students use a dictionary to look up more root words.

Book 5/Unit 4
How to Think Like a Scientist ⟋16

McGraw-Hill School Division

Fact & Nonfact

A **fact** is a statement that can be proven true using reference books, direct examination, an expert or your own experience. Sometimes a statement that may be true is a **nonfact** because it only expresses the author's personal opinion or the author's experience of a certain event. One way you can sometimes tell the difference between a fact and a nonfact is by asking yourself: *"Could I find this information in a reference book, such as an encyclopedia?"*

Read this letter. Then write whether you think each statement in the chart below is a fact or a nonfact. Explain the reason for your decision.

Dear Zackie,

Yesterday we went to the limestone cliffs. Looking at them, I was amazed how big and beautiful they were. Limestone is a really soft rock that crumbles easily. We found many pictures that people had carved into the cliffs hundreds of years ago. As we looked higher, we saw an eagle's nest perched on the edge of a cliff. The nest seemed as big as a refrigerator. And we saw the eagle. It was awesome! An eagle can have a wingspan of seven and a half feet! It makes you feel really tiny.

When we hiked to the top of the cliffs, our guide pointed out mountain lion tracks in the sand. They looked like the tracks of a big house cat to me. She told us that a full-grown mountain lion can weigh as much as 250 pounds! See you when we get back!

Julio

Statement	Fact or Nonfact	Explanation of Decision
1. Looking at them, I was amazed how big and beautiful they were.		
2. Limestone is a really soft rock that crumbles easily.		
3. Eagles can have a wingspan of seven and a half feet!		
4. She told us that a full-grown mountain lion can weigh as much as 250 pounds!		

At Home: Have students write two fact and nonfact statements from an article or movie review.

Vocabulary

Complete each sentence by writing a vocabulary word from the box on each line.

barrier	emerge	fireball	naturalist	parallel	teeming

1. The railroad tracks run _____ to each other.

2. The flower garden was _____ with butterflies of different colors and sizes.

3. Have you ever seen a butterfly _____ from its cocoon in the warm springtime?

4. The herd of sheep on the road acted as a _____ to the traffic and the honking cars made a terrible noise.

5. A great _____ erupted from the volcano and lit up the sky for a great distance.

6. We had a _____ as our guide on a field trip to the marshland that was to the north of our town.

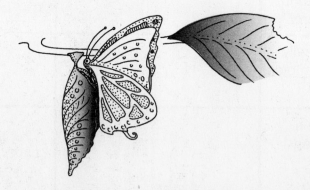

127   **At Home:** Have students use each of the vocabulary words in a sentence.

Book 5/Unit 4
An Island Scrapbook   6

McGraw-Hill School Division

School's Out!

Every Friday afternoon all the students *emerge* from the school doors. Suddenly the whole area is *teeming* with people laughing, running, and talking loudly. The safety monitors form a *barrier* along the sidewalk to keep younger students from wandering onto the driveway. The monitors line up within an arm's length of each other *parallel* to the road. They wear orange safety vests that are as bright as a *fireball*.

A *naturalist* watching this scene might be able to compare the activities to what goes on in a bee hive or ant colony.

1. What is a word that means "to come into view or appear"? _____

2. What does it mean to be *teeming with people* ? _____
   _____

3. What is a vocabulary word for *obstacle* ? _____

4. How is the word *fireball* used in this story? _____
   _____

5. Why would a *naturalist* compare the activity at the end of school on Friday to an
   insect colony? _____
   _____
   _____
   _____

5 Book 5/Unit 4
   An Island Scrapbook

At Home: Have students use the vocabulary words to write about something a naturalist might see.

127a

McGraw-Hill School Division

Story Comprehension

Think about what happens in "An Island Scrapbook." Then answer the questions below. For help you may look back at the story.

1. Who is writing this story? Who are the main characters? _____

_____

_____

2. Where does the story take place? _____

3. How do the author and her daughter spend their days together? _____

_____

4. Consider the title of this story. How are the handwritten notes pictured in the

illustrations different from the writing throughout the rest of the story? _____

_____

_____

_____

5. At one point in the story the author recalls a storm that happened on the island a few

weeks before, when she and Amy were alone in the summer house. What type of

storm was it? _____

6. What did they do after the storm happened? _____

_____

7. What types of crafts did Amy make that summer? What materials did she use for her

crafts? _____

_____

_____

8. What was the author's one rule about painting the things she found in nature? ____

_____

At Home: Have students create a craft or describe a gift
they'd like to create.

Use an Observation Chart

Scientists and naturalists use **observation charts** to collect and organize information. Observation charts help them to monitor and track what they are studying.

Use the observation chart to answer the questions below.

1. Which baboon is pregnant? _____

2. Which baboon is looking after Lu-Lu? _____

3. Which baboon took the grapefruits? _____

4. Which baboon is picking fights and taking food from the other baboons? _____

5. Which baboon is napping a great deal? _____

McGraw-Hill School Division

5 Book 5/Unit 4
An Island Scrapbook

At Home: Have students make an observation chart to collect information about what happens at dinner time.

129

Fact & Nonfact

A **fact** is a statement that can be proven true. A **nonfact** is a statement that may be true, but it expresses the author's opinion or personal experience and cannot be proven true.

Each statement below tells of something that happened in "An Island Scrapbook". Write **F** if it is a fact. Write **N** if it is a nonfact. You may look back at the story for help.

_____ 1. There are two high tides and two low tides every day.

_____ 2. The forest ground cover provides food and shelter for deer and birds.

_____ 3. The bright ocean continues on forever.

_____ 4. Barrier islands are long thin islands that run parallel to a coast.

_____ 5. We didn't sleep a wink the night of the hurricane.

_____ 6. Sea shells are beautiful.

Write two more facts and nonfacts that you can find in "An Island Scrapbook."
You may look back at the story for help.

Two more facts:

7. _____

8. _____

Two more nonfacts:

9. _____

10. _____

At Home: Encourage children to share the facts they discovered from "An Island Scrapbook" with a family member or friend. Have them discuss the difference between a fact and a nonfact.

McGraw-Hill School Division

Important & Unimportant Information

Nonfiction writing includes a great deal of **important** information that supports the main idea. There is also some **unimportant** information that makes the selection interesting or fun to read but does not directly support the main idea.

Read the paragraph below. Think about what the main idea is. Then write **I**, for important, next to each sentence that gives important information about the paragraph. Write **U** for unimportant information.

The school had a very successful car wash last weekend. We made more than $800 for charity. The students were well organized, which helped us wash so many cars. Many students wore waterproof coveralls or rain suits. Mr. Toya's class washed the most cars. The students enjoyed washing the cars and had only three water fights. The car wash wouldn't have been as successful if Ms. Myers' art class hadn't made signs advertising the event. They made beautiful neon-colored signs. You could read these signs from a block away. They spent hours putting them up early in the morning and then taking them down at night.

_____ 1. The school had a very successful car wash last weekend.

_____ 2. We made more than $800 for charity.

_____ 3. The students were well organized, which helped us wash so many cars.

_____ 4. Many students wore waterproof coveralls or rain suits.

_____ 5. Mr. Toya's class washed the most cars.

_____ 6. The students enjoyed washing the cars and had only three water fights.

_____ 7. The car wash wouldn't have been as successful if Ms. Myers' art class

hadn't made signs advertising the event.

_____ 8. They made beautiful neon-colored signs.

McGraw-Hill School Division

8 Book 5/Unit 4
An Island Scrapbook   **At Home:** Have students read an article and select a
sentence that gives important information.   **131**

Suffixes

A **suffix** is a word part added to the end of a word that changes the word's meaning. Knowing what a suffix means can help you figure out a word's meaning. The suffix *-less* means "not having" or "without". The suffix *-ment* means "the act or process of," "the place of a specific action," or "the state of a specific action."

Word	+	Suffix	=	New Word	Meaning
sleep	+	–less	=	sleepless	without sleep
arrange	+	–ment	=	arrangement	act of arranging

Write the suffix of each word. Write the word's meaning. Then use the word in a sentence of your own.

1. heartless   **Suffix:** _____   **Meaning:** _____

    Sentence: _____

2. excitement   **Suffix:** _____   **Meaning:** _____

    Sentence: _____

3. employment   **Suffix:** _____   **Meaning:** _____

    Sentence: _____

4. worthless   **Suffix:** _____   **Meaning:** _____

    Sentence: _____

5. tireless   **Suffix:** _____   **Meaning:** _____

    Sentence: _____

6. punishment   **Suffix:** _____   **Meaning:** _____

    Sentence: _____

7. encampment   **Suffix:** _____   **Meaning:** _____

    Sentence: _____

8. cordless   **Suffix:** _____   **Meaning:** _____

    Sentence: _____

At Home: Ask students to use two other words that end with *-ment* and two other words that end with *-less* in sentences.

Book 5/Unit 4
An Island Scrapbook 8

McGraw-Hill School Division

Judgments & Decisions

Scientists often test the **judgments** they make. These tests are called experiments. They base their final **decision** on the results of their experiments.

Read the following selection, and then answer the questions.

"There is a ghost in our new house!" Charlie cried. "I saw the attic door open by itself." "Honestly, Charlie!" said his older sister, Camilla. "There are no such thing as ghosts." "But I saw it," Charlie insisted. "The attic door opened, and no one was there." "Let's check it out," suggested Camilla. The old wood floorboards creaked as they walked along the hallway. They found the attic door ajar. Camilla had trouble shutting it. Fiddling with the doorknob, Camilla finally made the latch click and she securely shut the door. To make sure, she pulled on the knob. The door did not move.

"Charlie," Camilla instructed, "walk along the hallway, just like you did when the door opened."

Charlie walked down the hall. The floorboard right by the door creaked a little, and with a click the door opened.

"Ghosts!" Charlie cried.

"Hardly," said Camilla. She closed the door and asked Charlie to try it again. After a number of times walking past the door, Camilla proved to Charlie that if he walked past the door in a certain way, his weight shifted against the creaky floorboard to make the door pop open. The house did not have ghosts. It just had creaky, loose floorboards.

1. What happened that scared Charlie? _____

2. In Charlie's judgment, what caused the attic door to open? _____

3. Why didn't Camilla accept Charlie's idea about what made the door open? _____
_____

4. Camilla and Charlie had differing judgments about what made the door open. How did Camilla test Charlie's observation? _____
_____
_____

5. Why do you think that Camilla was successful in getting Charlie to change his mind?
_____
_____

Vocabulary

Complete each sentence with a vocabulary word.

atmosphere	collision	cycle	data	injured	uneven

1. The four seasons are an example of a natural _____.

2. We reached a conclusion using the _____ that we had collected during

   our science project.

3. There was a huge _____ when the car failed to stop at the red light.

4. Luckily, no one was _____ in the car crash.

5. The _____ of a county fair is exciting because there are many

   interesting activities.

6. The carpenter had to recut the boards because they were _____.

Spring

Summer

Fall

Winter

At Home: Have students use each of the vocabulary words
in a sentence.

McGraw-Hill School Division

Weather Forecasting

Predicting weather involves collecting and analyzing many kinds of *data*. Weather forecasters observe changes in the *atmosphere,* which is made up of oxygen, nitrogen, and other gases. By studying weather patterns, they learn what to expect from each *cycle* of weather events. This helps make their predictions less *uneven.* For example, they have to know what happens when a *collision* of cold air and warm air occurs. Weather reports are important because people can be *injured* or even killed by weather. So when you plan outside activities, make sure you listen to the weather reports.

1. What do you call the facts and figures that can be used to make decisions? _____

   _____

2. What is a word that means *the air or climate of a place*? _____

3. What are *uneven* predictions? _____

   _____

4. What does the word *cycle* mean as it is used in this story? _____

   _____

5. How can the weather forecast keep people from getting *injured*? _____

5

Book 5/Unit 4
The Big Storm

At Home: Have students write weather reports using the vocabulary words.

134a

Story Comprehension

Complete each sentence with information from "The Big Storm." You may look back at the story for help.

1. The westerlies are winds that blow in what direction across the United States?

_____

2. What does a barometer measure? _____

_____

3. What does a low-pressure reading usually mean? _____

_____

4. What different instruments do weather forecasters use to make their predictions?

_____

5. What atmospheric conditions can cause a tornado to occur? _____

_____

6. According to the map on page 477, where does the frigid air blowing into the United

States often come from? What type of weather conditions does it often bring?

_____

7. What do raindrops start out as inside of clouds? _____

8. What causes thunder to occur? _____

_____

Read a Weather Map

A national **weather map** shows the distribution of temperatures across the nation. Weather symbols for warm and cold fronts, high- and low- pressure areas, and precipitation also appear on the map.

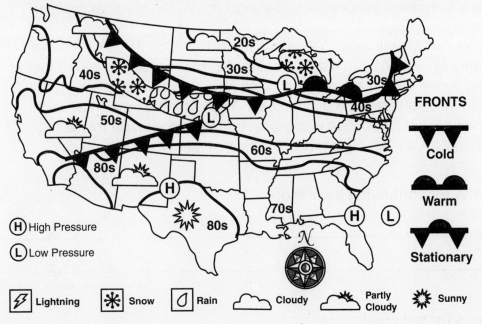

1. What does the symbol for a cold front look like? _____

   _____

2. What is the symbol for a high-pressure area (area of high atmospheric pressure)?

   _____

3. What temperature is forecast for most of Texas, in the south-central part of the

   country? _____

4. What kind of day will the Texas area have? _____

5. What will be the coldest temperature in the United States? _____

5 Book 5/Unit 4
The Big Storm   **At Home:** Have students use this map to tell what the
weather would be like where they live.   **136**

Judgments & Decisions

Before you make a **decision** about something, you consider the reasons for and against it. As you read the situation below, think of what you learned in "The Big Storm" and try to make the best decision. Write two reasons for each choice. Then make a **judgment** about what you should do. Write your final decision.

Suppose the following. You are in the Rocky Mountains on a cross-country ski trip and you hear a weather forecast predicting over 2 feet of snow during the night. You were planning a long ski trip tomorrow that would take you far into the mountains. You know the new snow might increase the danger of an avalanche, but you also realize this will probably be the last big snow of the ski season. What will you do?

Two reasons for continuing your trip:

1. _____

2. _____

Two reasons for not continuing:

3. _____

4. _____

Final decision:

5. _____

_____

Write a short paragraph about a situation in which you had to make tough judgments and decisions. Be sure to include two reasons for and against your actions, and then write about what your final decision was.

_____

_____

_____

_____

At Home: Encourage students to talk about their final decisions with a member of their family.

McGraw-Hill School Division

Draw Conclusions

When you **draw a conclusion**, you use facts from a story as well as your own knowledge and experience. Drawing conclusions as you read can help you better understand the story.

Read the selection below, and then answer each question. Describe the clues that helped you draw each conclusion.

> Angie and her twin brother, Carlos, decided to go shopping for presents for their parents. In the bookstore Angie saw a big book on the American Revolution that she knew her mother would love, but it cost way too much money for her to afford. Carlos picked it up and looked at the price, too. "Hey, if we combine our money, we could get this for Mom," said Carlos. They paid for their purchase and went into another shop.
>
> "Let's buy Dad something made from leather. He really likes leather," suggested Angie. But Carlos just walked out of the store. "What's the matter?" asked Angie.
>
> "When I have some more money, I want to buy Dad something special. Just from me. After all, he spent all his spare time helping me rebuild my bike," said Carlos.
>
> "I can understand that," said Angie. "Besides we probably don't have enough money left to buy dad a present now."

1. Do Angie and Carlos get along? _____

_____

2. Story clue: _____

_____

3. Experience clue: _____

_____

4. Do you think Carlos and his father are close? Explain. _____

_____

5. Carlos and Angie are doing something many people do, buying gifts for a family member. Why does this common experience help you draw conclusions about the characters? _____

_____

_____

5 Book 5/Unit 4
The Big Storm

At Home: Have students draw conclusions about what Carlos will do in the store.

138

Root Words

A **root word** forms the base of a longer word. Often a root word becomes another word when a prefix or a suffix is added to it.

For example: The word *scrib,* meaning "write," is a root word for *subscribe* and *scribble*.

Many root words in English come from Latin or Ancient Greek. Knowing the meaning of a root word and using context clues can help you define unfamiliar words.

Root Word	Meaning	Language of Origin
pute	to think	Latin
meter	measure	Greek
sphere	ball	Greek
dict	to say	Latin

Study the root chart above. Write the root of each word below.

1. computer _____   6. atmosphere _____

2. hemisphere _____   7. diameter _____

3. barometer _____   8. dictate _____

4. predict _____   9. biosphere _____

5. kilometer _____   10. verdict _____

Choose four words from above—one for each root word in the chart— and write a sentence for each one.

11. _____

12. _____

13. _____

14. _____

At Home: Encourage students to use a dictionary to look up the words they don't know from this list. Ask them to find out what "atmos" means.

139

Book 5/Unit 4
The Big Storm 14

McGraw-Hill School Division

Fact & Nonfact

A **fact** is a statement that can be proven to be true. A **nonfact** is something that is made up and can be proven to be false. When you read a story, one way you can tell the difference between facts and nonfacts is by looking for exaggerations in a character's behavior or abilities. You can also look for word clues such as, "This is hard to believe, but ..."

Read the story. Then complete the chart. Write whether you think a statement is a fact or a nonfact. Explain the reason for your decision.

I live in New York City. Every day we walk our dog in Central Park. With 340 acres of green space, it is one of the largest city parks in the world. Sometimes we ride our bikes there. My father's bike goes very fast. In fact, you might not believe this, but his bicycle can go faster than any car.

Our mother is a kite maker. She told us that human beings were flying kites before they discovered writing. One day she tested out a new kite. Well, you're not going to believe this either, but that kite caught hold of the wind and the next thing we knew, the kite was carrying our mother way above us. When she finally came down, she told us she had seen the Statue of Liberty. The statue is almost 151 feet high.

Statement	Fact or Nonfact	Explanation of Decision
1. Central Park has 340 acres of green space and a lake.		
2. My father's bicycle goes faster than any car.		
3. Human beings were flying kites before they discovered writing.		
4. The kite was carrying our mother way above us.		

4 Book 5/Unit 4
Catching Up with Lewis & Clark

At Home: Have students look for facts and nonfacts as they read.

140

Vocabulary

Complete each sentence with a vocabulary word.

bison	diaries	former	glistening	journal	superb

1. The coach keeps _____ every year to record his team's progress.

2. The movie was better than good— it was _____!

3. I keep a _____ to help me keep track of each day's events.

4. You can find herds of _____ out west in Yellowstone National Park.

5. Our _____ school principal came back to see our science fair.

6. Have you ever seen winter frost _____ in early morning light?

At Home: Have students use each of the vocabulary words in a sentence.

141

Book 5/Unit 4
Catching Up with Lewis & Clark   6

The Ranch

This just might be the best vacation we've ever had. It has been *superb* so far! This week we went to visit my mother's *former* professor, Ms. Berry. She lives on a ranch in the western state of Wyoming. We had to drive for miles up a dirt road to get to her place. On the way, we saw these huge shaggy creatures with horns.

"BUFFALO!" my brother cried. My mother turned politely and said, "Actually, Ms. Berry runs a *bison* ranch."

My brother immediately recorded this information in his travel *journal*. Every day he makes notes of new facts and the miles we've traveled. I'm keeping two *diaries*. I write in one at the end of each day, and I write in the other only when I have something important to say about what we've seen.

After lunch, Ms. Berry took us out to explore the ranch. This place looked very dry, so I was surprised to find a small pond. The water was a deep emerald green and was *glistening* in the sun. Staying at Ms. Berry's ranch was the perfect place to end our vacation.

1. What is a word that means "excellent"? _____

2. What does it mean that Ms. Berry was the mother's *former* professor? _____
_____

3. What is another word for the word "buffalo"? _____

4. How is a diary different from a *journal*? Consider how both words are used in
this story. _____
_____
_____

5. Why did it surprise the narrator to find a pond of *glistening* water in Wyoming? ____
_____
_____

5 Book 5/Unit 4
Catching Up with Lewis & Clark

At Home: Have students write about a vacation they would like to take using vocabulary words.

141a

Story Comprehension

Think about what happens in "Catching Up with Lewis & Clark." Then answer the questions below. You may look back at the story for help.

1. What did Meriwether Lewis and William Clark do nearly 200 years ago that no other United States citizen had done? _____

   _____

2. Where did they begin their journey? _____

3. Why did President Thomas Jefferson want Lewis and Clark to explore the area that was part of the Louisiana Purchase? _____

   _____

4. How long did it take the expedition to get to the ocean? How many miles did they travel? _____

5. Did the explorers set out on their journey all alone? Did they travel only on foot?

   _____

   _____

6. Who was Sacajawea? _____

7. Why was Sacajawea so important? _____

   _____

   _____

   _____

8. What makes it so difficult to find any trace of Lewis and Clark's journey? _____

   _____

   _____

McGraw-Hill School Division

At Home: Have students write a short report on Lewis and Clark.

Use a Map

Ghana is a country in western Africa. Look at the map of Ghana. Then use the map to answer each of the following questions.

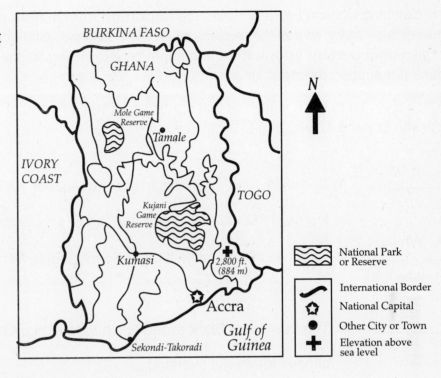

1. What is the national capital of Ghana? _____

2. What country is west of Ghana? _____

3. What country is east of Ghana? _____

4. What country is north of Ghana? _____

5. What are the two game reserves in Ghana? _____

6. What body of water borders Ghana? _____

7. What city is south of Accra?

_____

8. What is the highest elevation in Ghana, in feet and in meters? _____

_____

8 Book 5/Unit 4
Catching Up with Lewis & Clark

At Home: Encourage students to look up the African continent in an atlas or on a map of the world. Then have them locate Ghana.

143

Important & Unimportant Information

In "Catching Up with Lewis & Clark" the **important information** supports the main idea—*trying to find the remains of an old Lewis and Clark campsite.* There is also **unimportant information** that might be interesting for the reader, but does not support the main idea.

Place a ✓ next to each sentence that states important information for "Catching Up with Lewis & Clark."

_____ **1.** Scientists have been digging for remains of the Lewis and Clark journey in Great Falls, Montana, and Fort Clatsop, Oregon.

_____ **2.** Lewis and Clark made it possible for people from the East to settle the West.

_____ **3.** The Lewis and Clark expedition had to fight off bears and carry heavy canoes for weeks overland.

_____ **4.** Lewis and Clark kept maps and diaries, so scientists have a good idea where they might have camped.

_____ **5.** It took more than 500 days for Lewis and Clark to reach the Pacific Ocean.

_____ **6.** It is hard for scientists to say, "Lewis and Clark camped here," because the explorers left barely anything behind.

_____ **7.** Scientists have to sift dirt through a giant strainer to find things that might have belonged to Lewis and Clark on their journey.

_____ **8.** A number of monuments have been built to honor Sacajawea.

_____ **9.** The bison bone and pushpin are from the time of Lewis and Clark.

_____ **10.** Scientists think the ammunition and beads found at Fort Clatsop in Oregon might have belonged to the explorers.

At Home: Encourage children to talk about the most important information they learned from reading "Catching Up with Lewis & Clark."

144

Book 5/Unit 4
Catching Up with Lewis & Clark 10

McGraw-Hill School Division

Root Words

A **root word** forms the base of a longer word. Often a root word can form another word when a prefix or a suffix is added to it. For example, the root word *spect* meaning "to look" forms the words *suspect* and *speculate*.

Many root words in English come from Latin. By knowing the meaning of a root word and by using context clues you can define unfamiliar words.

Root Word	Meaning	Origin
quest	to seek	quaestus: from the verb *quaerere*, to seek or ask
memor	mindful	*memor:* Latin from Sanskrit, *smarati,* s/he remembers
origin	to arise	from the verb *oriri,* to rise or arise from

Study the root word chart above. Write the root word of each word below.

1. memorial _____
2. requested _____
3. original _____
4. remember _____
5. inquest _____

6. originate _____
7. questionnaire _____
8. memorize _____
9. aboriginal _____
10. memento _____

11. Is memor the root word of memento? How do you know? _____

_____

_____

12. Is origin the root word of memorial? How do you know? _____

_____

_____

At Home: Encourage students to use a dictionary to look up the words they don't know from this list.

Suffixes

A **suffix** is a word part that is added to the end of a word to change the word's meaning. Knowing what a suffix means can help you define words. The suffix *-less* means "not having" or "without". The suffix *-ment* means "the act or process of." "the place of a specific action" or "the state of a specific action."

Word	+	Suffix	=	New Word	Meaning
sleep	+	*-less*	=	sleepless	without sleep
arrange	+	*-ment*	=	arrangement	act of arranging

Write the suffix of each word. Write the word's meaning. Then use the word in a sentence of your own.

1. aimless   **Suffix:** _____   **Meaning:** _____

 Sentence: _____

2. government   **Suffix:** _____   **Meaning:** _____

 Sentence: _____

3. movement   **Suffix:** _____   **Meaning:** _____

 Sentence: _____

4. charmless   **Suffix:** _____   **Meaning:** _____

 Sentence: _____

5. regardless   **Suffix:** _____   **Meaning:** _____

 Sentence: _____

6. enslavement   **Suffix:** _____   **Meaning:** _____

 Sentence: _____

7. settlement   **Suffix:** _____   **Meaning:** _____

 Sentence: _____

8. spineless   **Suffix:** _____   **Meaning:** _____

 Sentence: _____

146

At Home: Ask students to use each of the words above in a sentence.

Book 5/Unit 4
Catching Up with Lewis & Clark   8

McGraw-Hill School Division

Unit 4 Vocabulary Review

A. Read each word in column 1. Find its antonym, or the word most nearly opposite in meaning, in column 2. Then write the letter of the opposite word on the line.

_____	**1.** injured	**a.** normal
_____	**2.** peculiar	**b.** current
_____	**3.** former	**c.** unusually
_____	**4.** normally	**d.** disappear
_____	**5.** emerge	**e.** cured

B. Supply the correct vocabulary word.

tortillas	automatically	barrier	cycle	atmosphere	collision	glistening

1. The snow on the trees was _____ in the bright sun.

2. Did you hear about that _____ between the train and the big rig?

3. Every morning when the alarm clock goes off, I get up and shower _____.

4. My parents make _____ in the morning for breakfast.

5. The four seasons are a yearly _____ in nature.

6. In order to be successful, you must learn to overcome any _____ in your way.

7. Some people really enjoy the busy _____ of a city.

12 Book 5/Unit 4
Unit 4 Vocabulary Review

At Home: Have students write a sentence for each vocabulary word in Part A.

147

Unit 4 Vocabulary Review

A. Answer each question.

1. What sort of an animal is a **bison**? _____

_____

2. What is **data** and what is it used for? _____

_____

3. What sort of things are **parallel** to each other? _____

_____

4. What do you find **unpleasant**? _____

_____

B. Write the vocabulary word that means almost the same thing as the underlined word.

swerved	observations	teeming	peculiar	naturalist	superb

1. The concert was <u>excellent</u>. You should go if you can. _____

2. The picnic basket was <u>swarming</u> with small insects. _____

3. Did the scientists make any <u>comments</u> about the event? _____

4. I want to become a <u>scientist who works with nature</u>. _____

5. I thought the chair looked <u>odd</u> painted pink. _____

6. We quickly <u>turned</u> our bikes to avoid the deeper mud puddles. _____

At Home: Have students write a question for each vocabulary word in Part B. Then have them answer the questions. They can use Part A as a guide.

148

Book 5/Unit 4
Unit 4 Vocbaulary Review
10

McGraw-Hill School Division

Compare & Contrast

When you **compare** and **contrast**, you pay attention to the ways in which two things are alike and different.

Read the paragraph about two types of bears. Then complete the compare and contrast chart below.

Black bears and grizzly bears are both North American bears. Black bears once were found all across North America, but now they mainly live in the mountains or forests. Grizzlies once roamed from Alaska to Mexico, but now they mainly live in protected forests in the western mountains.

Both kinds of bears have long snouts, stumpy tails, powerful jaws, and long, heavy claws. They both have shaggy fur, too. However, black bears have black fur, while grizzly bears have brown fur with white tips. Black bears are smaller. Black bears grow to six feet in height and can weigh 300 pounds. Grizzly bears, however, grow as tall as nine feet and weigh about 900 pounds. Most bears have poor eyesight and poor hearing, but they all have an excellent sense of smell.

Black Bears	Both Bears	Grizzly Bears
1. _____ _____ _____ 2. _____ _____ 3. _____ 4. _____ _____ _____	5. _____ _____ 6. _____ 7. _____ 8. _____ 9. _____ 10. _____ 11. _____ 12. _____ _____	13. _____ _____ 14. _____ _____ 15. _____ _____ 16. _____ _____

16 Book 5/Unit 5
The Riddle

At Home: Encourage students to make a compare and contrast chart for their two favorite cities.

149

Vocabulary

Complete each sentence with a vocabulary word.

apologized	debt	hasty	inquired	lamented	refreshment

1. After traveling for six hours on the bus, they stopped for a _____.

2. We were running so late that we only had time for a _____ lunch.

3. Pilar worked every Saturday to pay off the _____ that she owed.

4. The two tired hikers _____ about directions to the train station.

5. The class _____ the fact that their favorite teacher was retiring.

6. I _____ to the team for arriving to the game late.

At Home: Have students use each of the vocabulary words
in a sentence.

McGraw-Hill School Division

Moving On

We were very sad when our favorite neighbors had to move.

We *lamented* the fact that they were moving far away. As they had to start their new jobs immediately, their move was very *hasty*. We barely had time to plan a simple party with *refreshments* before they left.

Two weeks after they moved, our former neighbors wrote us a letter and *inquired* about their old neighborhood and about how everyone was doing. They *apologized* for not having had the time to really say good-bye. The neighbors felt like they owed us a debt for all the times that they had spent at our house. So they invited us to spend two weeks with them this summer. As they live on the beach, this should be a fun trip.

1. What is a word from the story that means mourned? _____

2. What does it mean to "make a *hasty* move"? _____

3. What kind of *refreshments* might have been served? _____

_____

4. What does the word *inquired* mean? _____

5. Why would the family that moved feel they had to *apologize*? What did they mean

by *debt*? _____

_____

_____

_____

5 Book 5/Unit 5
The Riddle

At Home: Have students use the vocabulary words to write a story.

150a

Story Comprehension

Answer the questions about "The Riddle."
Look back at the story to help you answer the questions.

1. What is the king doing in the forest when he gets lost? _____
_____

2. How does the king find where the charcoal maker lives? _____
_____

3. Is the charcoal maker surprised to see the king? How do you know? _____
_____
_____

4. Why does Anna apologize to the king? _____
_____

5. What is the debt that the charcoal maker has to pay back? _____
_____

6. How does the charcoal maker save for his old age? _____
_____

7. What does the charcoal maker mean by "throwing money out the window"?
_____

8. What does the king request of the charcoal maker? _____
_____

9. What does the king promise members of his court if they can solve the riddle?
_____
_____

10. Why does the charcoal maker finally tell the courtier the answer to the riddle?
_____
_____
_____

McGraw-Hill School Division

Follow Directions

When you are lost, you may want to ask for **directions.** Then you follow the directions to get to where you want to go.

Suppose you want to know how to get to the nearest public beach. Read the directions to the beach. Then answer the questions below.

Directions to the Beach

1. Continue north on this street about three blocks until you see the library.

2. At the library turn right and walk east for two blocks. You will come to a playground.

3. When you get to the playground, go through the green gate and cut across the playground to the orange gate on the other side.

4. When you walk through the orange gate, turn left and walk one block. You'll see a small fruit and vegetable stand under a big oak tree.

5. Just past the vegetable stand, you'll find a dirt road on your right. Walk down it. In a few minutes you will come to the sand dunes. From there you will see the path to the public beach.

---

1. Which way do you turn when you get to the library?

_____

2. What do you do when you get to the playground?

_____

3. What are you suppose to do once you cut across the playground?

_____

4. Which way do you turn from the orange gate?

_____

5. What do you do when you come to the fruit and vegetable stand?

_____

6. When will you be able to see the path to the public beach?

_____

6 Book 5/Unit 5
The Riddle

At Home: Have students write a set of directions from home to the public library.

152

Compare & Contrast

When you **compare** two things, you are pointing out how they are *alike*. When you **contrast** two things, you are pointing out how they are *different*.

Think about the charcoal maker and the courtier from "The Riddle."
Use the chart below to compare and contrast them.

Charcoal Maker	Both	Courtier
1. _____	5. _____	7. _____
2. _____	6. _____	8. _____
3. _____		9. _____
4. _____		10. _____

How would you compare the situation the charcoal maker and the courtier are in to the plot of a movie you have seen?

_____

_____

_____

_____

_____

_____

_____

At Home: Encourage students to create a compare-and-contrast chart for two characters, one from their favorite book and one from their favorite movie.

153

Book 5/Unit 5
The Riddle
12

McGraw-Hill School Division

Make Inferences

An **inference** is a conclusion or deduction made from evidence.
Readers make inferences about story elements based on details in the story or from their own experience. You usually "read between the lines" to figure out what a character is feeling or intends to do. When you make judgments or conclusions based on your reading you are making inferences about characters and events.

Read this selection. Then make inferences to answer the questions.

It was cold and damp where Julia and Marie had taken cover. They had to huddle close together for warmth. There was barely any light coming through the cracks in the old wood floorboards.

"Do you think it's past us yet?" asked Marie, still shaking. Julia put her arm around Marie.

"I don't know for sure," said Julia, "It's still dark. At least we don't hear it roaring like a train anymore. Let's wait a while longer. If we still don't hear anything, then I will climb the stairs and peek outside."

1. Where are Julia and Marie? How do you know? _____

_____

_____

2. What do you think the "it" is that Marie asks Julia about? Explain. _____

_____

_____

3. Why is Marie shaking? _____

4. Suppose Julia and Marie are sisters, who do you think is older? How can you tell?

_____

5. What can you infer about Julia's character? _____

5 Book 5/Unit 5
The Riddle

At Home: Have students choose a character from a movie or a book. Ask them to make inferences about how that character might act during a tornado, and explain why.

154

Context Clues

As you read, you can use **context clues** to help you define unfamiliar words.
Context clues are words in a story that give hints to what unfamiliar words mean.

Read each passage below. Use context clues to help define the underlined word.
Circle the letter with the correct meaning.

1. During the summer, we grow cabbage, corn, strawberries, and <u>fennel</u> in the garden.

Fennel is a kind of _____

   a. animal   **b.** plant   **c.** rock

2. When my grandparents returned from their trip to the island they brought back a

beautiful seashell as a <u>memento</u> of their trip.

A *memento* is a kind of _____

   a. candy   **b.** artwork   **c.** reminder

3. Orville and Wilbur Wright were two brothers who made and flew the first airplane.

They made it entirely from spare parts they found in their bicycle shop. They were

truly <u>ingenious</u> fellows.

You could replace the word *ingenious* with the word _____

   a. resourceful   **b.** lucky   **c.** scientific

4. I was disappointed when the cook handed me a <u>meager</u> portion of blueberry pie.

Everyone else had twice as much as I had.

Another word for *meager* is _____

   a. skimpy   **b.** plentiful   **c.** cold

5. Molten rock lies below the Earth's crust. When volcanoes erupt, this rock appears in

the form of <u>lava</u> and fire.

Lava is a kind of _____

   a. volcano   **b.** eruption   **c.** molten rock

At Home: Ask students to use context clues to figure out the
meaning of unfamiliar words from a magazine article.

Book 5/Unit 5
The Riddle 5

Author's Purpose and Point of View

The **author's purpose** is the reason for writing: to inform, entertain, or persuade.
The **point of view** is the perspective from which a story is told.
A **first-person point of view** uses the first-person pronouns: *I, me, we.*
A **third-person point of view** uses third-person pronouns: *he, she, they.*

Sometimes the point of view may not be obvious. For example, in nonfiction writing, the author will often talk directly to the reader. If you feel as if someone is talking directly to you, then assume you are reading the first person point of view.

Read each passage and complete the chart below. Then answer the questions.

A. If you come across a mountain lion while hiking, make yourself as large as possible. For example, raise your arms and the backpack or windbreaker you are wearing over your head. Do not crouch to the ground because then the lion will think you are about to attack. Do not run away immediately either, because then the lion might chase you, just for the fun of it. The best thing to keep the mountain lion from approaching you is to whistle while you walk away.

B. They should all vote for Andrea for class president. Andrea has already done so much for the class, so she deserves their support. She decorated the homeroom. She successfully organized a class trip. She has raised more money than anyone else for the new computer lab. She has also shown her leadership skills as captain of the softball team.

Passage	Author's Purpose	Author's Point of View
A	1. _____	2. _____
B	3. _____	4. _____

5. What would be the author's purpose for writing a play or movie? _____

6. What would be the author's purpose for writing a travel guide? _____

6 Book 5/Unit 5
Life in Flatland

At Home: Have students identify the purpose and point of view from a letter to the editor from a magazine.

156

Vocabulary

Complete each sentence with a vocabulary word.

landscape	distinguished	thickness	dimensions	trifle	unique

1. The _____ of the dining room were smaller than I had thought.

2. The gentleman in the tuxedo looked very _____ as he received his award for charitable work.

3. A thick fog hides the _____.

4. What is the _____ of your biggest textbook?

5. You should not _____ with your friend's emotions.

6. An iguana is a _____ kind of pet.

McGraw-Hill School Division

Dog Day Afternoon

I was painting a *landscape* in the park when a dog approached. I decided to toss a stick for it to chase.

"I wouldn't *trifle* with that dog if I were you," warned a voice.

I turned to see where the voice was coming from. But all I could see were trees.

"Up here," said the voice.

I looked up. There, in the *thickness* of the tree's leaves, I could vaguely make out a human form.

"I was measuring the *dimensions* of the new porch I am planning to add to that yellow house there," explained the voice, "when that dog chased me up this tree."

The house referred to could not be *distinguished* since all the houses were yellow. There was not a *unique* one among them.

1. What does *trifle* mean, as it is used here? _____

2. What is another word for "scenery"? _____

3. What was the person measuring before being chased up the tree? _____
_____

4. What do you call something that is the one of its kind? _____

5. Why was it hard to see the person in the tree? _____
_____

_____

5 Book 5/Unit 5
Life in Flatland

At Home: Use the vocabulary words to write about a strange event that happened to you.

157a

Story Comprehension

Read each statement. Write **T** if the statement describes the story "Life in Flatland." Write **F** is the statement does not correctly describe the story. If a statement is false, rewrite it to make it correct on the line provided. Look back at the story to help you.

1. _____ The author's pen name is Edwin Abbott.

_____

2. _____ Flatland is an imaginary place.

_____

3. _____ Flatland is a three-dimensional place.

_____

_____

4. _____ There are many different shapes in Flatland, but they all look like a straight line.

_____

5. _____ The most dangerous shape a Flatlander could have is an Equilateral Triangle.

_____

_____

6. _____ Flatlanders recognize each other by using the following three senses: sight, sound, and touch.

_____

7. _____ Fog is a curse in Flatland.

_____

8. _____ Flatlanders only go to the park when it is sunny.

_____

_____

_____

At Home: Draw a portrait of what you might look like in Flatland.

McGraw-Hill School Division

Read Signs

Signs provide all sorts of information. Wherever you go, signs tell you when or how to do things. Some signs warn you not to do things.

Read these two signs and then answer the questions below.

New Summer Hours for the Library
Monday: 10:00 A.M.- 7:00 P.M.
Tuesday - Thursday: 8:30 A.M.- 8:30 P.M.
Friday & Saturday: 8:30 A.M.- 4:30 P.M.
Sunday: CLOSED
Special Science Film Series:
2nd & 3rd Monday of each month, 6:00 P.M.

Welcome to Sunnyside Park
Open from dawn to dusk.
ATTENTION:
All dogs must be on leash except in the dog run.
PLEASE pick up after your dog.
Failure to pick up after or leash your dog will result in a fine of $50.
Repeated offenders will be banned from park.

1. Which day is the library closed? _____

2. If it is 5:15 P.M. on a Friday, do you have time to pick up a new book? _____

3. It is the third Monday of the month. What's happening at the library tonight? _____

4. Where is it okay for a dog to run off leash at Sunnyside Park? _____

5. What happens if someone gets caught not picking up after his/her dog? _____

6. What happens to people who repeatedly break the rules about dogs? _____

Author's Purpose and Point of View

Authors often write from a particular **point of view**, or perspective. Authors also have a **purpose,** or reason, for writing. An author's purpose for writing might be to persuade, to inform, to entertain, or a combination of the three.

"Life in Flatland" is a piece of fiction writing, yet the author wrote it as if he were writing nonfiction. He was trying to relate the narrator's personal experience about living in his world of two dimensions.

Review the story to answer the question below.

1. What is the point of view for "Life in Flatland"? How do you know? _____

   _____

   _____

2. What do you think the author's purpose was for writing "Life in Flatland"? _____

   _____

3. List three aspects of Flatland that seem real. _____

   _____

   _____

4. Why do you think the writer of "Life in Flatland" wrote about an imaginary world

   instead of just writing an essay about different dimensions? _____

   _____

   _____

5. What did you learn from reading "Life in Flatland"? _____

   _____

At Home: List three aspects from the story you enjoyed the most.   Book 5/Unit 5
Life in Flatland   5

McGraw-Hill School Division

Make Inferences

An **inference** is a conclusion or deduction made from evidence.

You usually "read between the lines" to figure out what a character is feeling or intends to do. When you make judgments or conclusions based on your reading, you are making inferences about characters and events.

Read this selection. Then make inferences to answer the questions.

It was the first day of the State Fair. While everyone else was rushing that morning, Sandy took her time. She dawdled in the bathroom, causing a line outside the door. At breakfast, she could barely bring the spoon of cereal to her mouth. While doing the breakfast dishes she moved as slowly as possible. It got to the point where her father barked at her to stop dragging her feet.

Finally, Sandy went outside to her father's truck. She peeked through the wooden slats at her favorite piglet. More than anything she wanted to rescue her "Pigita." Sandy had thought she could hide Pigita in the tree house for a few days, while she figured out a solution, but her father had found Pigita and put her back in the pen. Sandy's father had agreed to sell his pigs to a local pig farmer. He was meeting the farmer at the fair. It looked like Sandy had run out of time.

1. How does Sandy feel about going to the state fair? How do you know? _____

_____

2. Why does Sandy seem to have trouble eating her breakfast? _____

_____

3. Why does Sandy's father "bark" at her? _____

_____

4. Why does Sandy want to rescue Pigita? _____

_____

5. Why does Sandy's father put Pigita back in her pen? _____

_____

Prefixes

A **prefix** is a word part that can be added to the beginning of a word to change its meaning. Knowing what a prefix means helps you define the word. For example, look at the prefixes below. They are often used with root words to form words you might find in a math book.

Prefix	Meaning	Prefix	Meaning
tri-	three	*octa-*	eight
penta-	five	*poly-*	many
hexa-	six		

Use the prefixes above with the root word *angle* or the suffix *-gon*, meaning "angle," to identify the shapes below. Then write the name of each shape on the line with the same number. Explain the meaning of each word beside it.

 1   2   3   4   5

1. _____

2. _____

3. _____

4. _____

5. _____

At Home: Ask students to identify and define five other words with prefixes.

Book 5/Unit 5
Life in Flatland 5

Problem and Solution

Story characters often face **problems**. The plot is how the characters find **solutions** to their problems. Knowing how to find the problem in a story and the actions taken to solve it will help you better understand and appreciate a story.

Read the problems below. Then complete the chart by writing two ways you would solve each problem.

Problem	Solution
A. You are always misplacing your house key. What can you do?	1. _____ _____ _____
	2. _____ _____ _____ _____
B. You are shopping for groceries in the supermarket. While you are busy choosing apples, someone wanders off with your shopping cart by mistake. It is full of items you have selected. How do you get your shopping cart back?	3. _____ _____ _____ _____ _____
	4. _____ _____
C. One day, you ride your bike to the public library. You lock it to the rack outside with a chain. You try to unlock your combination lock but you can't remember the combination! How do you get your bike unlocked so you can ride it home?	5. _____ _____ _____ _____
	6. _____ _____ _____

McGraw-Hill School Division

6 Book 5/Unit 5
Tonweya and the Eagles

At Home: Encourage students to write about a problem and its solution to it.

163

Vocabulary

Use the vocabulary words to answer the questions.

1. **cleft**   Where is the cleft of a cave?

   _____

2. **consented**   What does it mean if you consented to something?

   _____

3. **defiantly**   When should you not behave defiantly?

   _____

4. **gratitude**   What do you feel gratitude for today?

   _____

5. **sacred**   Where would you find sacred objects?

   _____

6. **tribute**   For whom would you make a tribute?

   _____

164   **At Home:** Have students use each of the vocabulary words
           in a sentence.

Book 5/Unit 5
Tonweya and the Eagles   6

McGraw-Hill School Division

Growing Pains

One day, while putting away some things for my grandmother, I discovered a piece of paper poking out from a *cleft* in one of the attic beams. I removed the paper and brought it to my grandmother. She unfolded it and read it out loud.

Sometimes my folks act as if everything they say is sacred. If I dare disagree, they tell me to stop acting so defiantly. If just once they consented to let me have my way, I would be very happy. I feel a great deal of gratitude toward my parents for all they have done for me. I work hard to be the best person I can as a tribute to them. It's just that now that I am getting older, it's time for me to make a few of my own decisions.

"Why, this must be a page from your dad's boyhood diary," she said with a smile.

1. What does a *cleft* look like? _____

2. What does the word *sacred* mean as it is used here? _____

3. What does it mean to act *defiantly*? _____

   _____

4. What is another word for *consented*? _____

5. Why is it so important to be the best person you can be as a *tribute* to the people

   who care for you? _____

McGraw-Hill School Division

5   Book 5/Unit 5
Tonweya and the Eagles

At Home: Have students use the vocabulary words to write about gratitude.

164a

Story Comprehension

Review "Tonweya and the Eagles." Then answer the following questions. Note that the questions are divided into two parts: the foreword and the story about Tonweya.

Foreword

1. Who is the main character in the foreword? Is he any relation to the author?

_____

2. Where does the beginning of this true story take place? _____

_____

3. When do the events described in the foreword take place? _____

4. What is the purpose of the foreword? _____

_____

_____

Tale

5. Who is the main character in the tale? _____

6. Who is telling the story of Tonweya, and who is listening to it? _____

_____

7. What is the main problem in the tale? _____

_____

8. How does Tonweya get into trouble at the beginning of the tale? _____

_____

9. What happens in the middle of the tale? _____

_____

_____

10. How is the problem solved? _____

11. How does the tale end? _____

12. What is the purpose of this tale? _____

_____

At Home: Have students draw a picture for a scene described in either the foreword or the tale.

Book 5/Unit 5
Tonweya and the Eagles
12

McGraw-Hill School Division

Read a News Article

A **news article** is a newspaper story about an important news event based on facts. It always begins with a **headline** that is meant to catch the reader's attention. It also has a **dateline** that tells where and when the story was written.

Look at the news article below, then answer the questions.

Kids News Network

Tornado Strikes Worcester

By ALACHA McREA

BOSTON, March 28, 2001 – It looked like just another warm spring day in Worcester, Massachusetts, and Nancy Lopes had just stepped outside with her dog, Snoozer, to take a walk when she noticed a huge dark cloud approaching. Moments later James Lopes, her father, called out to her from the kitchen window and told her to hurry back inside. Mr. Lopes had just heard a tornado warning on the radio. The family quickly headed to the basement for safety.

The tornado soon touched down in their neighborhood. It tore the roof off of the Lopes's house as well as six others on their street. Their refrigerator landed in a tree a half mile away. Their car was destroyed when a giant oak tree crashed down on it. Power and telephone lines are still down. The family said they were glad no one was hurt and thankful that they heard the advance warning system on the radio.

1. What is the headline of the news article? _____

2. Where and when was the news story written? _____

3. Who is the news story about? _____

4. What city did the tornado hit? _____

5. What is the story about? _____

   _____

6. What was the family's reaction to the tornado? _____

   _____

At Home: Have students read a newspaper article and summarize it to a family member.

166

McGraw-Hill School Division

Problem and Solution

Writers often organize information in a story according to **problem and solution.** In "Tonweya and the Eagles," the main character, Tonweya, encounters a series of problems that are solved in surprising ways.

Describe the problem or solution in each box below.

Problem	**Solution**
Tonweya wanted to reach the ledge of a steep cliff in order to capture the eagles that nested there.	1. _____
Trapped on the ledge, Tonweya was afraid that he would roll off the narrow ledge when he was asleep.	2. _____
Tonweya saw that the eagles were just as hungry as he was.	3. _____
4. _____	Tonweya dreamed that the eagles, whom he had befriended, would help him get off the ledge.
5. _____	The eagles, who were now strong and big, safely carried Tonweya off the ledge.
6. _____	For two days Tonweya followed the trail leading to the new camp.

At Home: Have students retell the story, emphasizing the problems Tonweya faced and how he solved them.

McGraw-Hill School Division

Author's Purpose and Point of View

Authors have a **purpose**, or reason, for writing a story. An author's purpose might be to persuade, inform, entertain, or a combination of the three.
The **point of view** is the perspective from which a story is told.
The **first-person point of view** uses first-person pronouns: *I, me, we.*
The **third-person point of view** uses third-person pronouns: *he, she, they.*

Read each passage. Then complete the chart below and answer the questions.

   A. Birds of prey—like hawks, eagles and owls—are called raptors. They have sharp, curved bills and are excellent flyers. Raptors also have large, strong legs with powerful talons, or claws, for catching their prey. Since 1966, several raptors have been protected by law from being hunted.

   B. As your coach, I want you to know the gratitude I feel for you. It has been a difficult year. We have had to overcome many obstacles. Despite all the setbacks, however, each of you has given one hundred percent and done the very best you could. And that is the most a coach could ask for. Thank you very much.

Passage	What is the Author's Purpose?	What is the Point of View?
A	1. _____	2. _____
B	3. _____	4. _____

5. What would be the author's purpose for writing a mystery novel? _____

6. What would be the author's purpose for writing a speech about the benefits of

   recycling? _____

6

Book 5/Unit 5
Tonweya and the Eagles

At Home: Ask students to identify the point of view and author's purpose of a magazine article.

168

Context Clues

As you read, you can use **context clues** to help you define words. Context clues are words in a story that help define unfamiliar words.

Read each passage below. Use context clues to help define the underlined word. Circle the letter of the correct meaning.

1. Many claimed that it was her <u>destiny</u> to become a circus clown.

    You could replace the word *destiny* with the word _____

    a. privilege   **b.** fate   **c.** courage

2. They saved the buffalo hide to use as <u>parfleche</u> for making travel packs.

    Parfleche is a kind of _____

    a. blanket   **b.** leather   **c.** feather

3. Native Americans who lived in the Plains used to transport their belongings with a <u>travois</u>. This was a simple device made of two poles trailing from the horse, with a pouch in between.

    A *travois* is a kind of _____

    a. animal   **b.** shelter   **c.** carrier

4. The townspeople were <u>compelled</u> to do something to stop the rising flood.

    Another word for *compelled* is _____

    a. forced   **b.** interested   **c.** spoiled

5. The horse was so wild and <u>green</u>, he did not know what a saddle felt like.

    Green here means _____

    a. not brown   **b.** envious   **c.** inexperienced

6. Using bows and arrows, they hunted for <u>game</u> in the winter forest.

    Game here means _____

    a. a play   **b.** checkers   **c.** wild animals

At Home: Ask students to use context clues to define unknown words or terms in a favorite story.

Book 5/Unit 5
Tonweya and the Eagles
6

McGraw-Hill School Division

Compare & Contrast

When you **compare** things, you are pointing out how they are *alike*. When you **contrast** things, you are pointing out how they are *different*.

Read the paragraphs about birds of prey. Then fill in the compare-and-contrast chart below.

Eagles and falcons are birds of prey. Both birds are powerful flyers. They are similar to hawks. Eagles have long, broad wings, while falcons have long, pointed wings. Eagle wings are good for soaring. Falcon wings are good for swift flight. Falcons do not soar. Falcons are known for their bullet-shaped bodies, while eagles are known for their keen eyesight.

Both falcons and eagles keep their nests in high areas. Eagles make their own nests, but falcons use the nests of other birds. A female eagle lays one to three eggs, while a female falcon lays two to six eggs. When the eagle eggs hatch, the babies are cared for by both parents or just the female eagle. However, both the male and the female falcons take care of their young.

Eagles	Both Birds	Falcons
1. _____	6. _____	10. _____
_____	7. _____	_____
2. _____	_____	11. _____
3. _____	8. _____	12. _____
4. _____	9. _____	13. _____
_____	_____	
5. _____		14. _____
_____		_____
_____		_____
_____		_____

14 Book 5/Unit 5
Breaker's Bridge

At Home: Have students make a compare-and-contrast chart for their two favorite songs.

170

Vocabulary

Choose the correct word from the box to complete each sentence below.

dismay	gorge	immortals	murky	piers	scheme

1. The rescue divers could not see clearly through the _____ water.

2. The ancient Greeks thought Zeus, Apollo, and the other gods were _____.

3. The explorers stood high above the _____ where the river flowed between the two cliffs.

4. The ice-cold water swirled around the steel _____ of the bridge.

5. The children devised an elaborate _____ to surprise their parents.

6. With _____, we watched the other team score the winning basket against us.

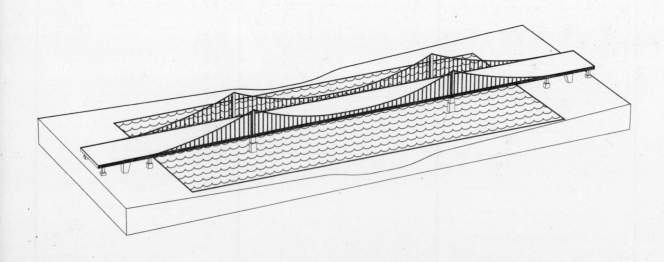

At Home: Have students use each of the vocabulary words in a one-page story.

Book 5/Unit 5
Breaker's Bridge 6

McGraw-Hill School Division

Wash Out

Many years ago, I worked on the mighty Colorado River. We had a great *scheme* for managing that river by building dams. However, one part of the river was hard to work in because the water was so swift. We had to build a bridge there so that trucks could cross the deep *gorge*.

I will never forget the day the dam gave way. We had just finished building two *piers* downstream from the dam. Just as we climbed up the cliff at the end of a long day, we heard a sudden, booming explosion. Then a wall of water came down the river in a flash. I can't tell you the *dismay* we felt when we looked at the destruction below us. Not even the *immortals* could have survived that. Luckily, no one was hurt, but all our work was lost. All we could see was the swirling, *murky* waters.

1. What is a word that means "dark or gloomy"? _____

2. What does it mean to have "a great *scheme*"? _____

3. What does the writer mean by the word *immortals?* _____

_____

_____

4. What does the word *dismay* mean? _____

_____

5. Why did they have to build two *piers* in the river? _____

_____

_____

5 Book 5/Unit 5
Breaker's Bridge

At Home: Have students use the vocabulary words to write a short story.

171a

Story Comprehension

Review "Breaker's Bridge." Then complete the exercise, filling in the characters, setting, and events from the story.

Characters

Breaker   1. _____

Emperor   2. _____

Old Man   3. _____

Setting

Time   4. _____

_____

Place   5. _____

Plot Events

Beginning   6. _____

_____

_____

Middle   7. _____

_____

_____

_____

_____

_____

End   8. _____

_____

_____

_____

_____

At Home: Ask students to write a story about a conflict over a bridge.

McGraw-Hill School Division

Read a Help-Wanted Ad

Many newspapers have classified sections where employers place **help-wanted ads**. A help-wanted ad is an advertisement that describes a particular job, the skills and experience that job requires, as well as where and how to apply. These ads also list the expected salary and hours of work.

ASSISTANT PARK RANGERS NEEDED

Now accepting applications for summer assistant park rangers. Must be able to start June 15 and work weekends. You must be responsible and willing to get your hands dirty. Farming or experience with horses a plus. Forty-hour work week, some part-time shifts available. Uniforms and work gloves provided. Apply in person only, at Park Ranger's office, weekdays 7 A.M.—6 P.M. or weekends 10 A.M.—2 P.M. No phone calls please.

---

1. What kind of job is being advertised in this help-wanted ad? _____

_____

2. Who placed the help-wanted ad? _____

3. Why do you think the people applying for this job have to be willing to get their

   hands dirty? _____

   _____

4. Would you apply for this job by sending a letter or telephoning the Park Ranger's

   office? Explain. _____

   _____

5. If you were available to work from 9 A.M.—1 P.M. three days a week, should you

   apply for the position? Explain. _____

   _____

6. Do you think someone who is interested in the environment should consider

   applying for this job? Explain. _____

   _____

6 Book 5/Unit 5
Breaker's Bridge

At Home: Have students write the help-wanted ad for their ideal summer job.

173

Compare & Contrast

When you **compare** two things, you are pointing out how they are alike. When you **contrast** two things, you are pointing out how they are different.

Think about the Old Man and Breaker from "Breaker's Bridge." Use the chart below to compare and contrast them.

Old Man	Both Characters	Breaker
1. _____ _____	4. _____ _____	7. _____
2. _____ _____	5. _____ _____	8. _____
3. _____ _____	6. _____ _____ _____	9. _____

Compare and contrast the old man with a superhero or good science-fiction character of today. How are they alike? How are they different?

_____

_____

_____

_____

_____

_____

_____

_____

174

At Home: Ask students to create a compare-and-contrast chart for two main characters from a story.

Book 5/Unit 5
Breaker's Bridge 12

McGraw-Hill School Division

Make Inferences

An **inference** is a conclusion or deduction made from evidence. You usually "read between the lines" to figure out what a character is feeling or intends to do. When you make judgments or conclusions based on your reading, you are making inferences.

Read this selection. Then make inferences to answer the questions.

Lew carefully took a step over the creaky threshold into his brother's room. Sam was sound asleep. Lew waited for his eyes to adjust to the darkness. Then he spotted the camera. Lew needed it for his class project, but Sam had said that he needed it, too.

On his second step, Lew tripped on a bicycle wheel in the middle of the room! He would have to be careful. There was plenty more to trip over—a box of old magazines, more bicycle parts, some tools, and an oil can. Lew could not believe how messy Sam was. Lew's room was the opposite.

The camera was finally within reach. Lew took a deep breath and reached his arm out, when suddenly—WHAM!—a pillow struck his back, throwing him off balance. As he heard a laugh, Lew knew talking his way out of this situation would not be easy.

1. What is Lew trying to do in his brother's room? _____

_____

2. What can you tell about Lew's brother, Sam? _____

_____

3. How are Lew and Sam opposites? _____

4. Who threw the pillow at Lew? _____

5. Reread the last sentence. What can you infer about the relationship between Sam

and Lew? _____

_____

_____

Prefixes

A **prefix** is a word part that can be added to the beginning of a word to change the word's meaning. Knowing what a prefix means can help you define a word. For example, the prefix *re-* means "again," "anew," "back," or "backward."

The prefix *in-* can mean *within, into,* or *toward.* The prefix *in-* can also mean *not.*

Prefix	+	Word	=	New Word	Meaning
re	+	new	=	renew	to make new again
in	+	side	=	inside	on the inner side, within something
in	+	complete	=	incomplete	not complete

Write the prefix of each word. Write the word's meaning. Then use the word in a sentence.

1. rebuild   **Prefix:** _____   **Meaning:** _____

   Sentence: _____

2. infield   **Prefix:** _____   **Meaning:** _____

   Sentence: _____

3. reconnect   **Prefix:** _____   **Meaning:** _____

   Sentence: _____

4. inset   **Prefix:** _____   **Meaning:** _____

   Sentence: _____

5. reschedule   **Prefix:** _____   **Meaning:** _____

   Sentence: _____

6. include   **Prefix:** _____   **Meaning:** _____

   Sentence: _____

At Home: Ask students to think of three other words with the prefix *in-* and three other words with the prefix *re-*. Have them use each word to write a short story.

176

Book 5/Unit 5
Breaker's Bridge   6

McGraw-Hill School Division

Problem & Solution

Characters in stories often face **problems.** The plot of the story is how the characters find **solutions** to their problems.

Read the problems below. Then complete the chart by writing down two ways to solve each problem.

Problem

Solution

You are at the movie theater. You buy two movie tickets for you and your friend. Then you go buy some popcorn. When it is time to hand over the tickets, you can't find them. What can you do?

1. _____
   _____
   _____
   _____

2. _____
   _____
   _____
   _____

You and a friend are walking your neighbors' dog in a big park. Suddenly, the dog, who is very big and very fast, breaks her leash and bolts away. You call for her, but she does not come. You see her chase another dog. You think you spot that dog's owner. You have to be in school in 15 minutes. What do you do now?

3. _____
   _____
   _____

4. _____
   _____
   _____

Suppose you live on the top floor of a very tall apartment building. You come home alone after school one day and realize that you forgot your key. No one is going to be home for several hours. You are hungry and have to finish a book report. What do you do now?

5. _____
   _____
   _____

6. _____
   _____
   _____
   _____

6 Book 5/Unit 5
Cleaning Up America's Air

At Home: Encourage students to write about a problem that they faced and their solution to it.

177

Vocabulary

Complete each sentence with a vocabulary word.

fumes	protective	regulations	standards	stricter	width

1. The coach wanted the players to follow new _____ for basketball.

2. We need to measure the _____ of the windows for new curtains.

3. The worst part about riding a bicycle to the baseball game is having to breathe the _____ from all the cars on the road.

4. This summer the local pool has even _____ rules about safety and conduct.

5. Kwame is very _____ of his younger brothers and sisters.

6. Ms. Wang sets high _____ for her science students.

At Home: Have students write a short story using each of the vocabulary words.

Silver's Air Test

Silver was wearing heavy *protective* clothing. She checked her oxygen supply one more time. Seeing the green light, Silver opened the turbocar door and began collecting air samples. Ever since the accident last week, Silver had to follow *stricter* rules of air collection.

The toxic *fumes* had made the air murky. According to the *regulations*, Silver had to take several air samples at different times of day. The device she used to take each sample was about the *width* of her thumb. Working late into the night, Silver could not help but wonder how much worse the air quality might have been without the *standards* set by the government.

1. What do you think Silver's *protective* clothing protected her from? _____

_____

2. What is one word that could mean more carefully enforced? _____

3. What is a simpler word for *regulations* ? _____

4. What does the word *width* mean as it is used in this story? _____

_____

5. Why do you think Silver wondered how much worse the air quality might have been

without the *standards* set by the government? _____

_____

5 Book 5/Unit 5
Cleaning Up America's Air

At Home: Have students use the vocabulary words to write five new sentences.

178a

McGraw-Hill School Division

Story Comprehension

Think about what you learned from "Cleaning up America's Air." Then answer the questions below. Look back at the story to help you.

1. What does EPA stand for? What is it? What does it do about air pollution? _____

_____

_____

2. What effects will the new EPA limits have on air pollution? _____

_____

3. Which is harmful, the ground-level ozone or the ozone high above Earth? _____

_____

4. Where do smog and soot come from? _____

5. What sort of health problems does breathing smog and soot cause? _____

_____

6. What can dust particles do to lungs? _____

7. How many people die each year in the United States partly due to air pollution?

_____

8. Why did some business people complain about the EPA's stricter standards to

control air pollution? _____

_____

9. How much does the EPA think it will cost to clean up the skies? _____

10. How many Americans now live in polluted areas? How many lives may be saved

with the new EPA standards for cleaner air? _____

At Home: Have students go to the library and research the EPA. What are three specific issues the EPA is combating?

Book 5/Unit 5
Cleaning Up America's Air /10

McGraw-Hill School Division

Read an Editorial

An **editorial** is a newspaper article in which the editors express their opinion about current events. An editorial is one writer's point of view that is supported with facts.

A Vote for Evening Basketball

City Council will decide tomorrow whether or not to support a bill funding evening basketball for teenagers. Here at *Wind City News*, we know that evening basketball programs have been successful.

For years now, many other cities across the nation have supported evening basketball for teenagers. Reports from these cities say that the program keeps teenagers out of trouble. In one city, teenage crime dropped by more than half.

While some people complain that there will be too much noise from these games, we at *Wind City News* believe it is better that teenagers are playing basketball rather than getting into trouble. As editors of the city's largest newspaper, we urge the City Council to vote in favor of this bill.

1. What issue will the City Council vote on? _____

_____

2. Who is writing the editorial? _____

3. What is the point of view expressed in the editorial? _____

_____

4. What fact does the editorial use to support its opinion? _____

_____

5. Why are some people opposed to evening basketball? _____

_____

6. How does the newspaper editorial respond to the complaints of those opposed to

the program? _____

_____

6 Book 5/Unit 5
Cleaning Up America's Air

At Home: Write an editorial about something you feel strongly about.

180

Author's Purpose and Point of View

"Cleaning Up America's Air" is a nonfiction story. The purpose of most authors of nonfiction is mainly to inform. As they present information, however, authors often express a **point of view**, especially when they are trying to persuade. Nonfiction writers can also write to entertain.

Answer the questions below from "Cleaning Up America's Air." Look back at the article to help you.

1. What is the author's main purpose for writing "Cleaning Up America's Air"?

_____

2. Does the author's point of view support the EPA's efforts to limit air pollution? How do you know? _____

_____

3. Can you identify places in "Cleaning Up America's Air" where the author presents a personal opinion? What does the author say? _____

4. Can you find an example in the article where the author is trying to persuade? If so, what is it? _____

_____

_____

5. If you were a factory owner who was not meeting EPA standards, would this article make you change your mind? Would you follow the EPA's stricter standards for limiting air pollution after reading this article? Explain. _____

_____

_____

At Home: Share what you learned about air pollution with a member of your family.

McGraw-Hill School Division

Context Clues

As you read, you can use **context clues** to help you define unfamiliar words. Context clues are words in a story that give hints to what unfamiliar words mean.

Read each passage below. Use context clues to help define the underlined word. Circle the letter with the correct meaning.

1. When you see smog hovering over a city, you are looking at ground-level <u>ozone</u>, a result of air pollution. This bluish, brownish gas has a strong, foul-smelling odor.

   Ozone is a kind of _____

   a. city skyline   **b.** gas   **c.** result

2. To reduce the number of cars on the road that contribute to air pollution, some people use <u>car pools</u> to commute to work.

   A *car pool* must be a form of _____

   a. government   **b.** a special car wash   **c.** transportation

3. Dust that is visible in the air is made up of large amounts of <u>particulate</u> matter.

   Something that is *particulate* must be _____

   a. too small to detect by itself   **b.** full of matter   **c.** green

4. My family lives next to the railroad tracks. Whenever a really heavy train goes by, the whole house <u>rumbles</u>.

   Another word for *rumbles* is _____

   a. shakes   **b.** fights   **c.** falls down

5. Whenever we have a school concert, we set up speakers to <u>amplify</u> the sound so that everyone sitting in the back can hear us.

   Amplify must mean to _____

   a. sit for a concert   **b.** set up for a concert   **c.** make sound louder

McGraw-Hill School Division

5 Book 5/Unit 5
Cleaning Up America's Air

At Home: Write three new sentences with context clues for three of the vocabulary words.

182

Prefixes

A prefix is a word part that can be added to the beginning of a word to change the word's meaning. Knowing what a prefix means can help you figure out what a word means. For example, the prefix *re-* means *again, anew,* or *back/backward.* The prefix *in-* can mean *within, into,* or *toward.* The prefix *in-* can also mean *not.*

Prefix	+	Word	=	New Word	Meaning
re	+	new	=	renew	to make new again
in	+	side	=	inside	on the inner side, within something

Write the prefix of each word. Write the word's meaning. Then use the word in a sentence of your own.

1. review   **Prefix:** _____   **Meaning:** _____

   Sentence: _____

2. react   **Prefix:** _____   **Meaning:** _____

   Sentence: _____

3. restart   **Prefix:** _____   **Meaning:** _____

   Sentence: _____

4. If the root word **vade** means *to go,* what does **invade** mean?

   Prefix: _____   **Meaning:** _____

   Sentence: _____

5. If the root word **spect** means *to look,* what does **inspect** mean?

   Prefix: _____   **Meaning:** _____

   Sentence: _____

At Home: Think of one other word that begins with the prefix *in-* and one other word with the prefix *re-*. Use each word to write a sentence.

183

Book 5/Unit 5
Cleaning Up America's Air
5

McGraw-Hill School Division

Unit 5 Vocabulary Review

A. Read each word in column 1. Find its antonym, or the word most nearly opposite in meaning, in column 2. Then write the letter of the opposite word on the line.

	Column 1	Column 2
_____	**1.** debt	**a.** clear
_____	**2.** unique	**b.** refused
_____	**3.** consented	**c.** credit
_____	**4.** murky	**d.** common
_____	**5.** stricter	**e.** easier

B. Write the correct vocabulary word from the list on each line.

apologized	gratitude	gorge	landscape	piers	regulations	trifle

1. We enjoyed biking through the rolling _____.

2. How many _____ will they have to build to take care of the increased traffic on

the river?

3. There are new building codes and _____ to follow this year.

4. You should have _____ for your mistake.

5. Thanksgiving is a time to express _____.

6. We rafted through the narrow _____.

7. I don't dare _____ with my cat when she is eating.

12 Book 5/Unit 5
Unit 5 Vocabulary Review

At Home: Have students write sentences for five vocabulary words.

184

Unit 5 Vocabulary Review

A. Answer each question.

1. What would it mean if you are one of the **immortals**? _____

2. What sort of things might be **lamented**? _____
_____

3. When is it a good idea to act **defiantly**? _____
_____

4. What sort of **standards** should be set for a classroom? _____
_____

B. Write the vocabulary word from the box that means almost the same thing as the underlined word.

distinguished	protective	hasty	inquired	scheme	tribute

1. The team made a <u>quick</u> retreat for the dugout when the rain started. _____

2. Someone came up with a really good <u>plan</u> for April's birthday. _____

3. We <u>asked</u> what they were doing for the science project. _____

4. The school is having a <u>ceremony to show thanks</u> for our principal. _____

5. It is good to be <u>caring</u> about your friends. _____

6. In ancient times, how were the planets <u>recognized as different</u> from each

other? _____

At Home: Write a question for six vocabulary words. Then answer the questions.

McGraw-Hill School Division

Judgments and Decisions

Before you can make a **decision**, you must consider your various choices and the reasons for and against the decision.

Read each situation below. List two reasons for each choice, and then make a **judgment** about what you should do. Write your final decision.

Suppose the following: You promised two friends that you would help them wash cars to raise money for your school's computer lab. Then you get an invitation to a birthday party from a boy you would like to be friends with. The party is the same day as the car wash. You really want to go to the party but you know that your two friends doing the car wash were not invited. What should you do?

Two reasons for helping with the car wash:

1. _____

2. _____

Two reasons for going to the birthday party:

3. _____

4. _____

Final decision:

5. _____

_____

At Home: Encourage students to write about situations where there have been more than one choice of decisions and how they made a final decision.

Vocabulary

Complete each sentence with a vocabulary word.

coax	escorted	navigate	nightfall	perished	ushered

1. We had to bicycle home before _____.

2. The city's mayor was _____ to the fundraising ball by her husband.

3. In the olden days, every ship's captain knew how to _____ by the stars.

4. The whole town _____ when the volcano erupted.

5. Have you ever had to _____ a frightened cat out of a tree?

6. Big celebrations _____ in the new year.

At Home: Have students use each of the vocabulary words in a sentence.

Book 5/Unit 6
Amistad Rising

6

Opening Night

It doesn't take much to *coax* me into attending the theater, especially on opening night. The first night of a play is the most exciting one. Almost everyone gets all dressed up. The play usually starts after *nightfall*. In the theater's lobby you may see dressed up people being *escorted* into the theater.

I'm careful as I *navigate* my way through the crowded lobby. If I'm with someone, I hold hands so we don't lose each other. As I enter the theater someone will hand me the playbill that tells me about the actors in the play. Then I will be *ushered* to the seats that are marked on my tickets. I expect I will enjoy the play, even though it's one in which all of the main characters will have *perished* by the end.

1. What is another word for *nightfall*? _____

2. What is a word that means "to persuade by urging"? _____

3. What does the word *navigate* mean, as it is used in this story? _____

   _____

4. What is the difference between being *escorted* and being *ushered*?

   _____

   _____

   _____

5. What does the writer mean when he says he will enjoy the show "even if everyone

   has *perished*"? _____

   _____

   _____

McGraw-Hill School Division

5   Book 5/Unit 6
Amistad Rising

At Home: Have students use the vocabulary words to write a short story about an opening night.

187a

Story Comprehension

Review "Amistad Rising." Then answer the questions below.

1. Who is the main character of "Amistad Rising"? Where was this person from?

   _____

   _____

2. When does this story take place? Is it a true story or not? How do you know?

   _____

   _____

3. What was Joseph Cinqué doing when he was captured and sold as a slave? Whom

   did he leave behind when he was forced into slavery? _____

   _____

   _____

4. What were conditions like on the slave ship? Give an example. _____

   _____

   _____

   _____

5. What happened to many of the enslaved Africans while they were on the slave ship?

   Explain. _____

   _____

6. What was the one event that made Joseph Cinqué decide to lead the rebellion on

   the Amistad? _____

   _____

   _____

At Home: Encourage students to write a summary for
"Amistad Rising" and to share it with a family member.
Students may create a visual retelling with a storyboard.

188

Book 5/Unit 6
Amistad Rising 6

McGraw-Hill School Division

Use the Card Catalog

A **card catalog** is a set of cards, in alphabetical order, listing all the books in a library. Each alphabetized card catalog has three different types of cards: author, title, and subject. **Author** cards list books by the name of the author. **Title** cards list all books by the title. **Subject** cards list every nonfiction book by its subject.

Complete the chart below. First, read what you are looking for in the left-hand column. Then, in the right-hand column, write what kind of card it would be best to search for: author, title, or subject. Write in the right-hand column what kind of card (author, title or subject) you would use to find the book.

What you are looking for	Best card to use
1. a book about Africa	1. _____
2. a book by Martin Luther King	2. _____
3. a book about slave ships	3. _____
4. a book called *Three Years Before the Mast*	4. _____
5. a book by Virginia Hamilton	5. _____
6. a book by Eloise Greenfield	6. _____
7. a book about safety on shipboard	7. _____
8. a book about the life of John Q. Adams	8. _____
9. a book by Jules Verne	9. _____
10. a book called *Building Your Own Ship*	10. _____

10 Book 5/Unit 6
Amistad Rising

At Home: Encourage students to use maps and locate favorite states and cities.

189

Judgments & Decisions

Think about some of the **judgments and decisions** made in "Amistad Rising." Answer each question below. Explain your answers. You may look back at the story.

1. When Joseph Cinqué and his fellow Africans were kept on the slave ship, they were forbidden to speak, so they whispered to each other. Do you think it was wise for them to do so? _____

_____

2. What is your opinion of Celestino, the cook, who signaled Joseph Cinqué that he and the other Africans would be killed? _____

_____

3. When the *Amistad* finally reached port after the uprising, the Africans on board were sent to a prison. Do you think it was right to send them to prison? _____

_____

_____

4. President Martin Van Buren did not want to upset southern slave holders by setting Joseph Cinqué free. So he made Joseph Cinqué and the other Africans face another trial. Do you think President Van Buren made the right decision? Explain. _____

_____

_____

5. Former President John Quincy Adams came out of retirement at the age of 72 to defend Joseph Cinqué. What does this action tell you about him? _____

_____

_____

At Home: Encourage students to discuss the story with a member of their family.

McGraw-Hill School Division

Draw Conclusions

When you **draw conclusions**, you use facts from a story as well as your own knowledge and experience. Drawing conclusions as you read can help you better understand a story.

Read the selection below, and then answer each question. Describe the clues that helped you draw each conclusion.

Every weekday Inga and her father walked into town together. She often had to rush to keep up with him. Inga noticed that her father always slowed down just as they got to the watchmaker's shop. There, in the front window, was a beautiful, marble chess set. Her father never said anything about it, but Inga could tell he admired it. She had seen her father's collection of faded newspaper pictures of him playing chess years ago. In them, he looked very serious as he played. Inga checked the price of the set and decided she would start saving her allowance.

Two days before her father's birthday, Inga watched closely as her father slowed down in front of the watchmaker's shop. This time he actually stopped and she heard him say, "It's gone." Inga had to hide her smile.

1. What sort of chess player was Inga's father when he was young? _____

_____

2. **Story clue:** _____

_____

3. **Experience clue:** _____

_____

_____

4. What happened to the marble chess set in the watchmaker's window? _____

_____

5. **Story clue:** _____

_____

6. **Experience clue:** _____

6 Book 5/Unit 6
Amistad Rising

At Home: Encourage students to draw conclusions about an article in the newspaper.

191

Context Clues

Context clues are other words in a story that help you define unfamiliar words. You can also look for familiar root words within larger words.

Read each passage below. Use context clues to help you define the underlined word. Circle the letter of the correct meaning.

1. Before the Civil War, the <u>abolitionists</u>, made up of whites and free blacks, spoke out for an end to slavery.

   An *abolitionist* must have been someone who was _____

   a. against the Civil War   **b.** against slavery   **c.** a free black

2. In a country far away, several newspaper reporters were held in <u>captivity</u> for seven years. They were sent to prison without any sort of trial, because the government claimed they were spies.

   Being held in *captivity* is the same as being _____

   a. kept in prison   **b.** in a country far away   **c.** a spy

3. The circus trainers put heavy, iron <u>shackles</u> around each leg of the powerful and angry bear. They hoped that would keep him from moving and hurting others.

   Shackles are used to _____

   a. provide iron   **b.** put bears in cages   **c.** keep something from moving

4. My parents are <u>reluctant</u> to let me go to the movies. They are not willing to let me stay out that late on a school night.

   Another word for *reluctant* is _____

   a. unwilling   **b.** eager   **c.** careless

5. We could hear the school chorus raise its voice in <u>unison</u>. It sounded so beautiful—everyone singing all at the same time.

   Unison must mean something done _____

   a. in a beautiful way   **b.** for a concert   **c.** in one voice

At Home: Encourage students to demonstrate how they can use context clues to figure out these unfamiliar words from "Amistad Rising": *provisions, quell, boon, indisputable, mutiny, savoring.*

Book 5/Unit 6
Amistad Rising   5

McGraw-Hill School Division

Cause and Effect

A **cause** is the reason why something happens. An **effect** is the result, or what happens. Many story events are connected through cause-and-effect relationships.

What might happen as a result of each story event below? Write the most likely effect of each cause on the line provided.

1. The class planted tiny flower seeds in the ground where it was sunny. Each day the students watered their new garden. They even made a scarecrow so that the birds wouldn't eat the seeds.

   Effect: ——————————————————————————

   ——————————————————————————————————

2. Sonya was rushing to get to her friend's house. She pedaled her bike as fast as she could along a quiet street near the town dump. She was going so quickly that she didn't notice when she rode her bike over a small pile of broken glass.

   Effect: ——————————————————————————

   ——————————————————————————————————

3. Juan is having a birthday party. His parents are sending out party invitations to everyone in Juan's class, to everyone in the school band, and to everyone on the softball team. Juan has many friends.

   Effect: ——————————————————————————

   ——————————————————————————————————

4. Dorea really wants to play the guitar. She has an older cousin who is a very good guitar player. Dorea decides to tell him that she wants to learn to play the guitar as well as he does.

   Effect: ——————————————————————————

   ——————————————————————————————————

5. Lew and Kim are good friends. Lew has been doing poorly on his math tests lately. Kim decides to help Lew study. They have been working together solving math problems every day after school.

   Effect: ——————————————————————————

   ——————————————————————————————————

McGraw-Hill School Division

Vocabulary

Complete each sentence with a vocabulary word.

husking	keg	landlord	oblige	rascals	sprawled

1. Those _____ are up to no good!

2. My father brought a _____ of root beer to the class picnic.

3. During the summer, my cousins in Nebraska spend hours _____ corn.

4. Everyone was _____ on their beach towels and relaxing by the pool.

5. Would you do anything to _____ a friend?

6. Our _____ said he has to raise the rent on our house next year.

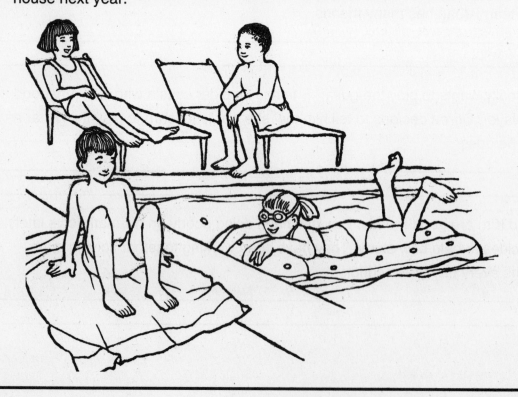

At Home: Use each of the vocabulary words in a sentence.

Book 5/Unit 6
Rip Van Winkle 6

McGraw-Hill School Division

Husking Bee

Rosa and Hank each sat on a *keg* as they worked. It was Saturday afternoon, and they were busily *husking* ears of corn. There was a huge pile of corn in front of them. They did this work for their *landlord*, Mr. Simpson, who owned the farm. Their work helped pay their rent on the farm.

"Those rascals never do their share of the work," complained Hank. He was referring to the laughing children *sprawled* on a haystack. They were the sons of Mr. Simpson.

"That's because they don't have to *oblige* anyone," commented Rosa. "They can spend their time doing as they please."

"Well, one thing's for sure," said Hank, "when I'm older, I'm going to own my own farm."

1. What is another word for *rascal*? _____

2. What is a word from the story that means "a small barrel"? _____

3. What does the word *husking* mean, as it is used in this story? _____

   _____

4. What does it mean to be "*sprawled* on a haystack"? _____

   _____

5. Why do you think Hank says what he does at the end? How do you think he feels

   about having to *oblige* the *landlord*? _____

   _____

   _____

At Home: Use the vocabulary words to write a short story
about having to oblige someone.

McGraw-Hill School Division

Story Comprehension

Review the play "Rip Van Winkle." Then complete the story chart below. For each scene in the play, describe the time and place of the setting. Then list the characters. Lastly, write a short summary of each scene.

Scene 1

1. **Setting:** Time: _____

   Place: _____

   _____

2. **Characters:** _____

   _____

3. **Summary:** _____

   _____

   _____

   _____

Scene 2

4. **Setting:** Time: _____

   Place: _____

5. **Characters:** _____

6. **Summary:** _____

   _____

   _____

   _____

At Home: Encourage students to act out a scene from "Rip Van Winkle" for or with family members.

Book 5/Unit 6
Rip Van Winkle 6

McGraw-Hill School Division

Use an Online Library Catalog

How can you find the library books you want? You can use an **online library catalog**. The online library catalog contains the information you need to find a book by its author, title, or subject.

Use the computer terminal below to answer the questions.

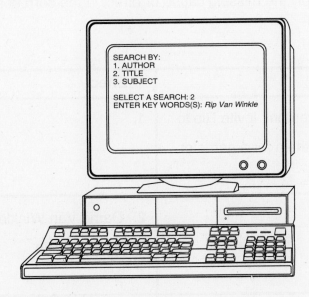

SEARCH BY:
1. AUTHOR
2. TITLE
3. SUBJECT

SELECT A SEARCH: 2
ENTER KEY WORDS(S): *Rip Van Winkle*

1. What category of search does the computer show? _____

2. Which category would you use to find a book by Washington Irving? _____

3. Which category would you use to find a book about clocks? _____

4. Which category would you use to find a book called *North American Folktales*?

_____

5. Suppose you want to search for a book by its author. Which number would you

   enter next to "SELECT A SEARCH"? _____

6. What key words would you enter to find books containing New York folktales?

_____

6 Book 5/Unit 6
Rip Van Winkle

At Home: Encourage students to go to the library with a family member and find a book using the online library catalog.

196

Cause and Effect

A **cause** is the reason why something happens. An **effect** is a result of the cause of what happens. Story events are often connected by a cause-and-effect relationship.

Complete the chart below to show the cause-and-effect links between events in "Rip Van Winkle." Supply the missing cause or effect in the correct column.

Cause	Effect
1. Vedder and Vanderdonk invite Rip to sit down and join them for a game of checkers.	1.
2.	2. Dame Van Winkle is angry with her husband Rip.
3. Rip forgets to mend the fence as his wife told him.	3.
4. Hendrik Hudson and his crew play ninepins up in the mountains.	4.
5.	5. Rip Van Winkle falls asleep for 20 years.
6.	6. Judith does not recognize her father at first.

McGraw-Hill School Division

At Home: Encourage students to share their knowledge of cause-and-effect relationships with a member of their family.

Book 5/Unit 6
Rip Van Winkle

 6

Draw Conclusions

When you **draw a conclusion**, you use facts from a story as well as your own knowledge and experiences. Drawing conclusions as you read helps you better understand a story.

Read the selection below, and then answer each question. Describe the clues that helped you draw conclusions.

> When Dana got home, she closely inspected the scrape on her knee. It wasn't very deep, although she could see a bit of sand in it. She still felt a little shaky about what had happened.
>
> "That's the problem with biking on that sandy road," Dana reminded herself. "It's too slippery." Dana sighed. It would be a while before she would want to go biking again.
>
> While washing off her knee in the bathroom, Dana heard some loud seagulls outside. She looked out the bathroom window and saw a large group of seagulls that seemed to be playing in the waves. She smiled to herself. She may not want to go biking, but when her knee healed, she could still go swimming.

1. Where does Dana live? _____

2. **Story clue:** _____

3. **Experience clue:** _____

   _____

4. What happened to Dana's knee? How did she scrape it? _____

   _____

5. **Story clue:** _____

   _____

   _____

6. **Experience clue:** _____

   _____

   _____

McGraw-Hill School Division

⬜6 Book 5/Unit 6
Rip Van Winkle

At Home: Have students draw conclusions about a magazine article.

198

Synonyms and Antonyms

Synonyms are words with the same or similar meaning and are used for different situations. **Antonyms** are words with the opposite or nearly opposite meaning and are used for contrast, or to show differences.

Use the words in the box to create pairs of synonyms and antonyms. Then list the pairs in the columns below.

warm	enter	hot
lazy	soft	idle
merry	exit	jolly
loud	cold	repair
fix	break	
village	town	

Synonyms

1. _____
2. _____
3. _____
4. _____
5. _____

Antonyms

6. _____
7. _____
8. _____
9. _____
10. _____

Compare the underlined words in each sentence. Write whether they are antonyms or synonyms.

11. If you keep being <u>idle</u>, people will think you are <u>lazy</u>. _____

12. Read the poem out <u>loud</u>, but speak with a <u>soft</u> voice. _____

At Home: Use a thesaurus to find an antonym or synonym for each vocabulary word in "Rip Van Winkle."

Book 5/Unit 6
Rip Van Winkle

12

McGraw-Hill School Division

Sequence of Events

Events in a story happen in a certain **sequence** or order. By recognizing that sequence you can make better sense of a story.

Read the short story. The story chart below lists the story events out of order. Number each event in the correct sequence.

One sunny day, Tanika and Jamal rode their bikes to the State Fair. When they got to the fairgrounds, they discovered that there was a long line for tickets.

First they locked their bikes. Then they waited in line. While they were waiting they talked about the rides they would take. They had enough money to buy tickets for two rides and popcorn. Jamal really wanted to ride on the ponies. Since it was almost his birthday, they rode the ponies first. Tanika really wanted to go on the Ferris wheel, so that was their second ride.

While they were riding the Ferris wheel, Jamal and Tanika saw dark clouds approaching. As soon as they got off the Ferris wheel, it got windy, and started to rain. They ran for the nearest telephone booth where they called their uncle to come pick them up.

Sequence	Event
	Tanika and Jamal wait in line to buy tickets.
	They see dark clouds approaching.
	Tanika and Jamal lock up their bikes.
	They go on the Ferris wheel.
	They ride the ponies.
	They call their uncle to come pick them up.
	Tanika and Jamal ride their bikes to the State Fair.
	The wind and rain start.

8 Book 5/Unit 6
Sea Maidens of Japan

At Home: Have students identify the sequence of events of a book or movie.

200

Vocabulary

Complete each sentence with a vocabulary word.

cove	disgrace	driftwood	flails	host	sizzle

1. For several days after the storm, _____ washed up on the beach.

2. You can hear the pancake batter _____ as you plop it in the hot skillet.

3. The lifeguard knows a swimmer is in trouble if he or she _____ both arms in the water.

4. My dad will be the _____ of the next neighborhood meeting.

5. The small ship found a safe _____ in which to anchor during the storm.

6. The team played well, so it was not a _____ that they lost the game.

The following vocabulary words are scrambled. Write each unscrambled word on the line.

7. iflsal _____

8. scragide _____

9. veco _____

10. dowordfit _____

McGraw-Hill School Division

At Home: Have students use each of the vocabulary words in a sentence.

Book 5/Unit 6
Sea Maidens of Japan   10

A Day at the Beach

My cousin Juan was the *host* of a beach party. He invited me to come. I had never been to that beach before. After we dug a barbecue pit in a sandy cove, we watched burgers and fish sizzle on the grill.

After lunch I searched for small pieces of *driftwood*, I saw my older cousin Tomás swim into the deep water beyond the cove.

"Isn't he swimming out a little too far?" I asked his sister, Marta.

"Don't worry unless he *flails* his arms," she said. "Tomás is a strong swimmer. Besides, he wouldn't do anything careless. He wouldn't want to *disgrace* himself."

1. Who is the *host* at the beach party? _____

2. What other foods do you know that might *sizzle*? _____

3. How does *driftwood* get to the beach? Where does it come from? _____

   _____

4. What is one word that means "a small, sheltered bay"? _____

5. Why should they only be worried if Tomás *flails* his arms? Why would that be a

   disgrace for Tomás? _____

   _____

   _____

McGraw-Hill School Division

At Home: Have students make a collage using pictures or symbols to represent the vocabulary words as used in this story.

Story Comprehension

Answer the questions about "Sea Maidens of Japan." You may want to look back at the story for help.

1. Whose voice is the narrator of "Sea Maidens of Japan"? _____

_____

2. Who is Okaasan? What does she do for a living? _____

_____

3. What is Okaasan trying to teach Kiyomi? Why does Okaasan tie a rope around

Kiyomi's waist? _____

_____

_____

4. What do Kiyomi's two older sisters do for work? Did they choose to follow the *ama*

tradition, too? _____

_____

5. What does Kiyomi do while waiting alone on the shore as her mother dives for

seafood? _____

_____

6. What does Okaasan take Kiyomi to see in the middle of one night? _____

_____

7. What happens when Kiyomi has to make her first deep water dive with the *ama*?

_____

_____

8. What is so special about the sea turtle that swims with Kiyomi when she finally

makes a deep water dive with the *ama*? _____

_____

At Home: Let students act out a scene from "Sea Maidens of Japan."

McGraw-Hill School Division

Choose Reference Sources

When you want information, you can choose from a number of different
reference resources: almanac, atlas, dictionary, encyclopedia, and thesaurus.

An **almanac** is a book of up-to-date facts about important people, places, and
events. It is published each year.

An **atlas** is a book of maps. It gives information about different places in the
world.

A **dictionary** tells you the definition and pronunciation of words. It lists the words
in alphabetical order.

An **encyclopedia** is a set of books containing articles about important people,
places, things, events and ideas.

A **thesaurus** is a book of synonyms—words with the same, or almost the same,
meaning. Sometimes it also lists antonyms—words with opposite meanings.

---

1. In which reference book would you look to find out how to pronounce the word

   tread? _____

2. Where would you look to find out about the feeding habits of sea turtles?

   _____

3. Where would you look to find synonyms for the word *pry*? _____

4. In which book would you be able to find maps of all the world's oceans?

   _____

5. Where might you look to find out the birthday of your favorite musician?

   _____

Book 5/Unit 6
Sea Maidens of Japan
5

At Home: Encourage students to talk about the different
reference resources. Have them write about each one
compared to using a computer for research.

203

Sequence of Events

Events in a story happen in a certain **sequence** or order. Below is a story chart listing events from "Sea Maidens of Japan." Number each event in the order in which it happened in the story.

Sequence	Event
	Kiyomi smiles as a wave sweeps the grown sea turtle back to deeper waters.
	Okaasan starts teaching Kiyomi to dive and fish along the coral reef.
	Kiyomi cannot make herself jump from the boat on her first deep water dive with the *ama*.
	Kiyomi finishes her first successful deep water dive with the *ama*.
	Okaasan takes Kiyomi out at night to watch the sea turtles lay their eggs.
	Kiyomi puts white cream on her face to protect it from the cold, salty water.
	Kiyomi eats shellfish on an island beach with the other *ama*.
	Kiyomi guides the confused baby sea turtle to the water.
	Kiyomi recognizes the star on the grown sea turtle's back.
	Kiyomi is afraid to jump into the deep water.

At Home: Have students explain where they would include the scene of Kiyomi pretending to host a tea ceremony for mermaids in this chart.

204

Book 5/Unit 6
Sea Maidens of Japan

10

McGraw-Hill School Division

Cause and Effect

A **cause** is the reason why something happens. An **effect** is the result, or what happens. Many story events are connected through cause-and-effect relations.

What might happen as a result of each story event below? Write down the most likely effect of each cause.

1. Sea turtles planted their eggs in the sand where the sun would keep the eggs warm. Volunteers then guarded the beach where the eggs were laid. They made sure no harm could come to the eggs.

   Effect: ————————————————————————

2. Andrea would become forgetful after she played too many computer games. One night she decided to make a cake after she finished playing her favorite game. When she put the cake in the oven to bake, she forgot to set the timer.

   Effect: ————————————————————————

3. Julio has to quickly get to the school bus stop or he will miss the bus. On his way, he decides to stop at the newsstand for a quick look at one of his favorite magazines. He reads an entire article before he leaves.

   Effect: ————————————————————————

4. Jim is getting ready to run in a big race. Naturally, he is a little nervous. He even forgot to tie a double knot in his laces, the way his coach told him to. In the middle of the race, Jim suddenly feels the laces on one of his sneakers come free.

   Effect: ————————————————————————

5. It is the day before the last big spelling test of the year. Amanda decides that she would much rather fly her new kite than study for a test.

   Effect: ————————————————————————

Context Clues

Context clues are words or sentences in a story that help you define unfamiliar words.

Read each passage below. Use context clues to help define the underlined word.
Circle the letter of the correct meaning.

1. Many people eat abalone. Abalone live in shells. Some people call them shellfish,

   but <u>abalone</u> aren't any type of fish.

   An *abalone* must be similar to a _____

   a. small plant   **b.** snail   **c.** frog

2. After high school, Sonny found a job at the local <u>cannery</u>. He ran one of the big

   noisy machines that fill cans with all sorts of food.

   A *cannery* must be like a _____

   a. factory   **b.** can of food   **c.** big loud, machine

3. My great-grandparents used to harvest seaweed along the shore. They used the

   plant for soup. Nowadays, <u>kelp</u> is used to make all sorts of things.

   Kelp must be a kind of _____

   a. shell   **b.** fish   **c.** seaweed

4. We had to use a crowbar to <u>pry</u> open the heavy metal door.

   To *pry* something is to _____

   a. hammer it into place   **b.** use force to open it   **c.** make a good try

5. Even though the rest of the class tried to <u>muffle</u> their laughter by putting their hands

   over their mouths, Suki could hear them laughing.

   When people *muffle* their laughter they are trying to _____

   a. make it sound louder   **b.** make it sound silly   **c.** hide the sound of it

McGraw-Hill School Division

At Home: Encourage students to demonstrate how they used context clues to figure out these unfamiliar words from "Sea Maidens of Japan."

206

Book 5/Unit 6
Sea Maidens of Japan

5

Judgments & Decisions

Before you make a **decision**, you consider the reasons for and against the decision. Read each situation below. List two reasons for or against each choice, and then make a **judgment** about what you should do. Write your final decision.

Suppose the following: You have a small collection of favorite books. One of your friends asks to borrow a book from your collection. When you notice your friend is holding a tattered magazine, you remember that last year this same friend borrowed a book, and it came back battered and worn. Although your friend apologized and even offered to replace the book, you said not to bother. Your friend has lent you his things in the past. Do you think you should lend this same friend a book this time?

Two reasons for lending your friend another book:

1. _____

2. _____

Two reasons against lending your friend another book:

3. _____

4. _____

Final decision:

5. _____

_____

_____

_____

5 Book 5/Unit 6
The Silent Lobby

At Home: Encourage students to discuss how they made their final decisions.

207

Vocabulary

Complete each sentence with the correct vocabulary word.

interpret	pelted	persuade	register	shabby	soothing

1. We had to _____ our parents to let us camp out in the backyard.

2. Some kinds of music have a _____ effect and can help you relax.

3. The teacher asked us to _____ the poem.

4. As we drove through the storm, hail _____ our windshield.

5. On the first day of college, many students have to wait in a long line to _____ for classes.

6. My old winter coat looked _____ compared to the new one my brother wore.

At Home: Have students use each of the vocabulary words in a sentence.

Batter's Up!

Every spring, our softball team has to *register* with the city league. The coach usually takes us all downtown in our uniforms to sign up.

This year we wanted to *persuade* our coach to buy us new uniforms because the old ones were looking *shabby*. My friend Alfonzo tried to tell our coach that the league rules stated uniforms "could not be torn, stained, or faded." The coach wanted to know how he managed to *interpret* that from the rule book.

"Well, maybe we could get the hardware store to support us," the coach suggested in a *soothing* voice.

We were all so happy with the coach's idea that we playfully *pelted* each other with our softball gloves.

1. What is another word for *persuade* ? _____

2. What is a word that means "one way of explain the meaning of something"?

_____

3. What does the word *soothing* mean, as it is used in this story? _____

_____

4. What would you hear if hail *pelted* a car roof? _____

_____

5. Why doesn't the team want to register in their old uniforms? What are they going to

do about it? _____

_____

_____

5

Book 5/Unit 6
The Silent Lobby

At Home: Have students use the vocabulary words to write a short story, poem, or song lyrics.

208a

Story Comprehension

Review or reread "The Silent Lobby." Then answer the questions below.

1. Who is telling the story of "The Silent Lobby"? Explain. _____
   _____
   _____

2. Why didn't Craig's mother want him to go to Washington, D.C.? _____
   _____

3. What did they make Craig's father do when he tried to register to vote? Explain what
   happened. _____
   _____
   _____

4. Who is Mrs. Fannie Lou Hamer? What did she do? _____
   _____
   _____

5. What happened to the 83,000 votes that African Americans cast during Mississippi's
   1964 election? What about the people they voted for? _____
   _____
   _____

6. How would this story have been different if the doorman hadn't let the people from
   Mississippi take shelter from the rain in the tunnel? Explain. _____
   _____
   _____

At Home: Encourage students to make a storyboard to retell
"The Silent Lobby."

Book 5/Unit 6
The Silent Lobby
6

McGraw-Hill School Division

Use the Library

If you look for a book at the library, you will probably find it easiest to search for the book by call number. The call number tells you where to find the book on the library shelf. Most libraries use call numbers from the Dewey Decimal System.

Dewey Decimal System	
000-099	Generalities (encyclopedias, magazines, etc.)
100-199	Philosophy and Psychology
200-299	Religion
300-399	Social Sciences (economics, sociology, law, education, customs, etc.)
400-499	Language (language, dictionaries, grammar)
500-599	Natural Sciences and Mathematics (astronomy, physics, chemistry, earth science, biology, math, etc.)
600-699	Technology and Applied Sciences (medicine, engineering, business)
700-799	The Arts/Fine and Decorative Arts (architecture, sculpture, painting)
800-899	Literature and Rhetoric (novels, poetry, plays, criticism)
900-999	Geography and History

1. Which numbers might contain information about oil painting? _____

2 In which category could you find an English dictionary? _____

3. Where would you look for information about the biology of plants?

   _____

4. In which category would you expect to find a book titled *The History of the Original Thirteen Colonies*? _____

5. Where would you look for *The Book of Poetry*? _____

6. Suppose you have a book with a call number of 150. What might the book be about? _____

6 Book 5/Unit 6
The Silent Lobby

At Home: Have students go to the library and find one book in two different categories of the Dewey Decimal System.

210

Judgments & Decisions

Think about some of the **judgments and decisions** that people made in "The Silent Lobby." Answer each question below. Explain your answers. You may want to look back at the story for help.

1. Mr. Clem told Craig's father that he would fire him if he tried to register to vote. Craig's father decided to register to vote. Did Craig's dad do the right thing? Explain.

   _____

   _____

   _____

2. Do you think the Governor of Mississippi made the right decision when he threw out all the votes that African Americans had cast in 1964? Explain. _____

   _____

   _____

3. What is your opinion of Mrs. Fannie Lou Hamer, who decided to set up the Mississippi Freedom Democratic Party? Explain. _____

   _____

   _____

4. Do you think the doorman at the Capitol who refused to let in the people from Mississippi was making a fair decision to block them from entering? Explain.

   _____

   _____

   _____

5. During the vote in Congress, Craig decided to sit on his hands as he watched. Do you think this was wise of him? _____

   _____

   _____

   _____

McGraw-Hill School Division

Draw Conclusions

To **draw a conclusion** when reading a story, you use facts from a story as well as your own knowledge and experience. Drawing conclusions as you read can help you better understand a story.

Read the selection below, and then answer each question. Describe the clues that helped you draw conclusions for question 1.

> Naseem rested his head on one arm. On the kitchen table before him was a blank sheet of paper. Crumpled papers were all over the floor under the table. Fatima pushed aside a mound of library books and sat down.
>
> "Listen, Naseem, you just have to tell yourself, 'You can do it!' Fatima said. "Look, you've done all the research."
>
> Naseem lifted his head and stared outside the kitchen window.
>
> "You have until tomorrow morning," she reminded him. "If you just pick up the pen and start writing now, you'll be OK—as long as you just stop tossing away everything you write." Fatima uncrumpled one of the papers. "And I'd use this, if I were you," she suggested as she handed him the outline.

1. What is it that Naseem has to do? How can you tell? Write the clues that helped

   you below. _____

2. **Story clues:** _____

   _____

3. **Experience clues:** _____

   _____

4. How is Naseem feeling? How can you tell? _____

   _____

   _____

5. What kind of person is Fatima? How can you tell? _____

   _____

McGraw-Hill School Division

5 Book 5/Unit 6
The Silent Lobby

At Home: Encourage students to share how they used drawing conclusions to answer these questions.

212

Synonyms and Antonyms

Synonyms are words with the same, or nearly the same, meanings and are used for different situations.

Antonyms are words with opposite, or nearly opposite, meanings and are used for contrast or to show differences.

Divide the words in the box into pairs of synonyms and antonyms and then write each pair under the correct column below.

shabby	soothing	elect	beaten
gawked	returned	alarming	pelted
left	right	stalling	threadbare
wrong	moving	lobby	vote
awake	asleep	stared	persuade

Synonyms

1. _____
2. _____
3. _____
4. _____
5. _____

Antonyms

6. _____
7. _____
8. _____
9. _____
10. _____

Compare the underlined words in each sentence. Are they antonyms or synonyms.

11. While the traffic was <u>moving</u> quickly all around us, our car kept <u>stalling</u>.

_____

12. My favorite sweater began to look <u>shabby</u>. Even the patches on the elbows were

<u>threadbare</u>. _____

At Home: Encourage students to use a thesaurus to decide if the words protested and pleaded are synonyms or antonyms. Have them explain.

Book 5/Unit 6
The Silent Lobby
12

McGraw-Hill School Division

Sequence of Events

Events in a story happen in a certain **sequence** or order. By recognizing that sequence you can make better sense of a story.

Read the short story. The story chart below lists story events that are out of order. Number each event in the correct sequence.

Arnie has a job delivering newspapers to his neighbors in the morning. He gets up before sunrise to start his work. It is still dark when he rides five blocks to the newspaper truck. There, Mr. Popkin loads 50 newspapers onto the red wagon attached to the back of Arnie's bike. Then Arnie spends almost two hours riding his bike up and down the streets in his neighborhood.

When he gets to Mr. Hanson's house, he finds a blueberry muffin waiting for him in the newspaper basket. Mr. Santiago greets Arnie at his fence, because he knows Arnie is scared of the Santiago's big barking dogs. Mr. Santiago hopes someday Arnie will not be afraid of the dogs. Poor Arnie always hands him the paper and rushes off.

When he arrives home, Arnie's dad has breakfast waiting for him. Arnie puts the blueberry muffin in the cupboard, deciding he'll eat it later.

Sequence	Event
	Arnie decides to keep the muffin in the cupboard and to eat it later.
	Arnie is scared of the Santiago's dogs, so he hands the paper to Mr. Santiago and rushes off.
	Mr. Popkin loads Arnie's wagon with newspapers.
	Arnie rides his bike five blocks to the newspaper truck.
	Mr. Santiago greets Arnie at his fence.
	Arnie finds a blueberry muffin waiting for him at Mr. Hanson's.
	Arnie arrives home and eats breakfast.
	Arnie gets up before sunrise.

At Home: Have students identify the sequence of events of a favorite book or movie.

McGraw-Hill School Division

Vocabulary

Complete each sentence with a vocabulary word.

confirmed	lush	variety	isolated	tropical	wonderland

1. The _____ storm brought warm waters into the North Atlantic.

2. For the school dance, we decorated the gym to look like a magical _____.

3. With one phone call, the newspaper reporter _____ that the rumor

   was not true.

4. After living in the desert for years, I longed for a _____ green garden.

5. Who would want to live in an _____ cabin deep in the woods?

6. The bookstore downtown sells a _____ of posters and postcards, as

   well as books.

215

At Home: Have students use each of the vocabulary words
in a sentence.

Book 5/Unit 6
Amazon Alert! 6

Secret Garden

Reporters *confirmed* today that there is indeed a secret garden in the desert. Traveling to an isolated cottage on the outskirts of a small desert town, they discovered what one reporter called a *wonderland*.

"In the back of the abandoned cottage is a high stone wall that is clearly falling apart," claimed one reporter. "We were surprised to find what we did behind it."

"When we walked out of the cottage's back door and into the garden, it was like walking into a *tropical* forest," said the reporter. "I have never, in all my life, seen such a *variety* of plants and flowers. There were several kinds of palm trees and brightly colored birds flew among the trees. How could such a *lush* place survive in a desert?" Then, at the edge of the garden we saw a large well.

1. What does it mean if something is *confirmed*? _____

2. What sort of cottage is an *isolated* one? _____

   _____

3. What does the word *variety* mean as it is used in this story? _____

   _____

4. What is one word that means "typical of the warmer regions of Earth"? _____

   _____

5. What makes this "secret garden" a *lush wonderland*? _____

   _____

   _____

McGraw-Hill School Division

Story Comprehension

Answer the questions below about "Amazon Alert!" You may refer back to the story.

1. How big is the Amazon rain forest? Give the area in square miles. _____
_____

2. How much of our planet's fresh water supply does the Amazon hold? _____
_____

3. What is deforestation? Who is responsible for it in the Amazon region? _____
_____

4. Why do people in Brazil burn down trees in the Amazon rain forest? _____
_____

5. How much of the rain forest has been destroyed so far? _____
_____

6. What is the government of Brazil doing about the destruction of the Amazon rain
forest? _____
_____

7. Why did deforestation slow down in 1996 and 1997? _____
_____

8. Whose way of life in the Amazon is in danger of disappearing? _____
_____

At Home: Share what you have learned about the Amazon
rain forest with a member of your family.

McGraw-Hill School Division

Use an Encyclopedia

An **encyclopedia** is a research tool. It is a set of books containing articles about important people, places, things, events, and ideas. The articles are arranged by alphabetical order in volumes. When you use an encyclopedia to find facts about a topic, you must have a "key word" in mind. Look at the illustration to answer the questions.

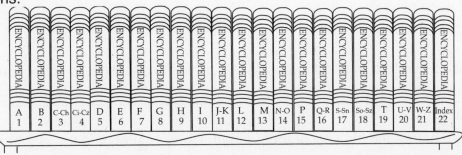

1. Why would you want to use an encyclopedia to write a report about something?

_____

_____

2. If you wanted to research information on the history of kites, what key word would

you use to find your subject? _____

3. In which volume would you look for information about *costumes*? _____

_____

4. In which volume would you look for information about the history of the United

States? _____

_____

5. Which volumes do you think might have articles about French painters and artists?

Explain. _____

_____

_____

_____

McGraw-Hill School Division

5 Book 5/Unit 6
Amazon Alert!

At Home: Encourage students to use a key word to research information in an encyclopedia and share their findings with a family member.

217

Cause and Effect

A **cause** is the reason why something happens. An **effect** is the result, or what happens. Many story events are connected through cause-and-effect relationships.

What might happen as a result of each story event below? Write down the most likely effect of each cause.

1. Doug woke up late and decided to skip breakfast so he could get to school on time.

   Effect: ————————————————————————————

2. It is the night before the big soccer tournament. Gerry is spending the night at Aziz's house. They stay up really late talking about how well they want to play in the game tomorrow. Their team plays early in the morning.

   Effect: ————————————————————————————

   ————————————————————————————————————

3. Lee and Sue are busy working on their tree house when they notice a beehive on one of the branches above them. Sue tells Lee that if they leave the bees alone, the bees will leave them alone. Lee decides to try to remove the beehive with a broom.

   Effect: ————————————————————————————

4. Anita's sneakers no longer fit. She does not like to shop and is feeling impatient. She asks the clerk for the same style sneaker she always wears. Anita does not bother to try the new sneakers on in the store. She just buys them and leaves.

   Effect: ————————————————————————————

   ————————————————————————————————————

5. Tanya poured twice as much milk as she should have into the muffin mix.

   Effect: ————————————————————————————

McGraw-Hill School Division

Synonyms and Antonyms

Synonyms are words with the same, or nearly the same, meaning. **Antonyms** are words with opposite, or nearly opposite, meaning.

Divide the words in the box into pairs of synonyms and antonyms and list them in the correct column below. You may use some words more than once.

area	modern	repair	slow
construction	preserve	rich	swift
destruction	protect	save	traditional
lush	region	shield	damage

Synonyms

1. _____

2. _____

3. _____

4. _____

5. _____

6. _____

Antonyms

7. _____

8. _____

9. _____

10. _____

Compare the underlined words in each sentence. Write whether they are antonyms or synonyms.

11. There was so much <u>damage</u> to the house that we could not <u>repair</u> it.

_____

12. As we traveled through the southwestern <u>region</u>, we discovered that most of the

<u>area</u> was a vast desert. _____

Context Clues

You can use **context clues** to help you define unfamiliar words.

Read each passage below. Use context clues to help you define the underlined word. Circle the letter of the correct meaning.

1. Many <u>ecologists</u> went to study the effects of pollution on wildlife.

   An *ecologist* must be a kind of _____

   a. firefighter   **b.** scientist   **c.** lawyer

2. During the 1980s, many rock bands made music videos. There was a huge growth in video sales during that <u>decade</u>.

   A *decade* must last _____

   a. a couple of years   **b.** ten years   **c.** 100 years

3. We entered the giant cave. The guide explained that this was a <u>habitat</u> where many bats lived.

   A *habitat* must be a kind of _____

   a. animal behavior   **b.** plant   **c.** community where animals live

4. The problem in the Amazon rain forest is that people <u>abuse</u> the resources there. That is what is destroying the region.

   To *abuse* is to _____

   a. use wrongly   **b.** treat fairly   **c.** be resourceful

5. The people in the village want to <u>modernize</u> the local water supply by putting in an electric water pump.

   To *modernize* must mean to _____

   a. keep supplying water   **b.** make things better   **c.** make things up-to-date

6. Sometimes you have to <u>sacrifice</u> what you really want for the sake of something or someone else.

   To *sacrifice* must mean to _____

   a. give something up   **b.** want something   **c.** understand

At Home: Make a list of context clues you used to define any unfamiliar words you found while reading "Amazon Alert!"

Book 5/Unit 6
Amazon Alert!

6

McGraw-Hill School Division

Unit 6 Vocabulary Review

A. Read each word in column 1. Find its antonym, or the word most nearly **opposite** in meaning, in column 2. Then write the letter of the opposite word on the line.

	Column 1	Column 2
_____	1. perished	**a.** made up
_____	2. disgrace	**b.** new; in good condition
_____	3. shabby	**c.** honor
_____	4. rascals	**d.** survived
_____	5. confirmed	**e.** honorable people

B. Write the correct vocabulary word on each line.

escorted	isolated	oblige	persuade	sizzle	soothing	tropical

1. How can I _____ you to let me borrow your CD player?

2. To _____ my parents, I do all my chores before they tell me to.

3. The old artist lived on an _____ ranch about 35 miles from any town.

4. As the blizzard raged, I dreamed of visiting a _____ island.

5. Sometimes a hot bath can be _____.

6. Our father _____ my sister to her first concert.

7. While warming butter for the sauce be careful that you don't let it _____ and burn.

McGraw-Hill School Division

12 | Book 5/Unit 6
Unit 6 Vocabulary Review

At Home: Write a sentence for each vocabulary word in Part A.

221

Unit 6 Vocabulary Review

A. Answer each question on the line below the question.

1. Why would you have to *coax* someone? _____

_____

2. If you were *sprawled* on a couch, how would you feel? _____

_____

3. What does someone look like when he or she *flails*? _____

_____

4. What does it mean to *interpret* a poem? _____

_____

B. Write the vocabulary word that means almost the same thing as the underlined word or words.

host	husking	navigate	pelted	register	variety

1. The tugboat had to <u>find its way</u> across a crowded, foggy harbor. _____

2. We discovered a <u>number of different kinds</u> of butterflies in the garden. _____

3. We thanked the <u>person who invited us</u> for the wonderful meal. _____

4. We <u>struck</u> each other with snowballs. _____

5. The kitchen crew is out back <u>removing the husks from</u> all the corn. _____

6. How old do you have to be to <u>sign up</u> to vote in the United States? _____

At Home: Write a question for each vocabulary word in Part B. Then answer the questions. You can use Part A as a guide.

222

Book 5/Unit 6
Unit 6 Vocabulary Review /10